THE FOOD V
herbs in nutrition

an anthology by
Maria Geuter

Celebrating 100 years since her Birth

The Food We Eat
herbs in nutrition.
an anthology by:
Maria Geuter 1895-1980.
Centenary edition.

Herb illustration by: Lisa Walters & Andrew Geuter.

ISBN 0-9524403-3-4

Collected, Revised and Edited by: H. & T. Clement.

Published by:
Anastasi^{Ltd}, Broome Nr. Stourbridge W.M. DY9 0HB.

The Food We Eat:-a series of essays, was first published 1939/40 /41 Sun-field   Letters.
Herbs in Nutrition:- was first published in 1962 and reprinted in 1970/72 Second Edition 1978 Reprinted 1990. Published by the Bio-Dynamic Agricultural Association (ISBN 0-9503780-6-2.)

Typeset by: *Anastasi*^{Ltd.} .

Printed and Bound in Great Britain by:
Biddles ^{Ltd.}
Guildford and King's Lynn.

Cover by: **Andy Oldacre**
Drawing of Vegetable. & Fruit Man, by: Artist unknown.

INTRODUCTION TO THE 1995 CENTENARY EDITION.

Maria Geuter 1895 — 1980

Maria Geuter was born and grew up in a large family in Germany—During the first World War she nursed at the hospital of Meschede in Westphalia. There she met Fried Geuter, whom she married, and Herbert Hahn who introduced them both to Anthroposophy. After the war they all went to live in Stuttgart—Herbert Hahn became one of the founding teachers of the Waldorf School and Fried joined Der Kommende Tag, an Anthroposophical economic enterprise. Maria had her first child Herbert, in 1919 named after Herbert Hahn and in 1921 and 1924 two daughters. A few years later Fried moved to Switzerland to study Curative Education and became a curative teacher—In 1929 he brought this new teaching to England and in 1930 Maria joined him. Fried and Michael Wilson had opened a home for children with special needs, Sunfield, in Selly Oak, Birmingham, and Maria undertook the catering and household management. Being used to hard times from her experiences during the inflation in Germany, she fed the little household with wonderful skill and economy. She had what amounted to genius in the manner in which she could produce the most satisfying meals with the slenderest of means. She continued to feed our growing family when the home moved to Clent. There she took a leading part in managing the gardens, and also gave classes in nutrition. She had a group of very good cooks with whom she worked intensively, just a few of them are Mary & John Kobbe, Helen Sucher, Maragret Martin, Ilsa Gemina, Joan Rudel, Hazel Straker, Edna Williams. Maria also wrote essays and poems, some set to music, by Michael Wilson, and then performed at festivals.

In her later life, when living at Broome Farm, she was in demand as a lecturer in many places in the UK including Emerson College, and the USA. She also wrote articles and finally her well known book "Herbs in Nutrition". Everything with Maria was quite individual—she had remarkable qualities all her own. Her articles and her book are unique—they all grow naturally out of the spirit of Anthroposophy itself.

"... She had the wonderful qualities of reverence and devotion, even for the smallest simplest things. To see her while cooking, for instance, admiring with such reverence the beautiful forms of the inside of a piece of fruit or vegetable, was a revelation. Rudolf Steiner tells us that when the qualities of *reverence* and *devotion* are encouraged during childhood they develop in old age into the capacity to bless and the strength for a life of activity.[1] This certainly seems to apply in the life of Maria Geuter. ...-... It seemed that what she herself put into the preparation of the food, the *love* and *devotion* as well as the knowledge she had gained from past experience was what made all the difference. ..."[2]

She had many close friends, apart from those already mentioned, the following:-

Cynthia Chance,	Gwen Loader
Mr.& Mrs. E. Edmonds	Helen Martin
Ned & Ann Evetts	Lothar Marx,
Herbert Hahn,	Paul Nordoff
Rudolf & Margaretha Hauschka,	Walter Johanus Stein,
Eileen Hutchins	Mr. & Mrs. Van-Bemelen,
Countess Keyserlingk,	Dr. Walter
Dr. & Mrs. Kolisko,	Ita Wegman,
Ernst Lehrs,	Michael Wilson

to name but a few.

In this Centenary edition we have tried to bring together some of Maria's most interesting written work on food. The essays in the series "The Food We Eat" were written in war time Britain, yet still they are very modern and up to date, full of interest. The second half is a slightly revised reprint of her book "Herbs in Nutrition". This book has been in print and selling regularly ever since it came out in 1962.

It is our hope that the reader will approach this book with an open mind and without prejudice or preconception. Rather let the thoughts expressed therein settle in the soil of

---

[1]   Book "Metemorphoses of the soul vol.1: Paths of Experience" Lecture IV "The Mission of Reverence" Rudolf Steiner Press 1983
[2]   From a tribute to the memory of Maria Geuter by Helen Martin, The Three Roses 1980

your mind, as seeds in the soil of the field, there to wait until the conditions are right; then germinating, sprouting forth to produce fruit and bounty for future generations.

The term "nutrition" in this book has a broader meaning than the normal, formal scientific and material sense of proteins, carbohydrates, vitamins, etc.; it is here meant in a far wider holistic way, taking all the senses into account also the environment in which we live and how we grow our food. Yes, the way we grow our food, is of the greatest importance for our nutrition, along with where it originates, from an animal, fish, mushroom, plant, salt. For example if we take the sugar from the plant, it makes a real difference whether sugar is extracted from the root, stem, leaf, fruit or flower (honey) as to how it nourishes the human being. The sugar from root beet, feeds the head and thinking, whereas the stem and leaf cane sugar feeds the lung, circulatory system and emotions, and the fruit, flower and honey, feeds the muscles, limbs, and will, etc. The same is true of other foods. Here it can be seen how subtle and delicate these processes are, and consequently if the way the food is grown, is mineralised and filled with subtle poisons, this brings the whole plant down into a sub-root state.

Then difficulties and health problems can arise when the true "nutrition" is thrown out of balance or is laced with minerals or artificials. No matter whether they enter the food on the farm and garden or in processing, preserving, colouring, flavouring or cooking to the point it enters the mouth, the food can be thrown out of balance. Even if outwardly it appears balanced, and complete.

One other point we would like to make is the role of truth! If you think about when someone has told you a lie, an untruth about something, and when you find out, well, to say the least, it hurts! This is what is happening to our sensory body when it is fed substitute or artificial colouring, flavouring, sweeteners, etc. The food, (or in reality the cook), is telling a lie and this causes stress in the deeper workings of the human being leading to health problems.

Today we are faced with lies, illusions and falsehoods in all areas of our life not just in our food, but in books, film, TV, news papers, music, etc. even our own thoughts. All this attacks us, and leaves our inner being filled with uncertainty, and with a hollowed out feeling, a sense of despair.

In this book Maria shows us in a humble, but most helpful way, how we can start to bring things back into harmony. By bringing the ART of HEALING back into our food in a simple modest way, that we can all achieve.

Enough of the heavy stuff. Maria has written this material out of a very wise and knowing heart which so many have cherish and enjoyed. Read on and Bon appetit!

TABLE OF CONTENTS

Herbs in Nutrition

PREFACE

to the 1978 edition.

The content of this book is based on many years of practical work in the kitchen and the study of herbs and their relationship to our food. It first appeared in 1962 in response to numerous requests for guidance on the use of herbs in nutrition, since when it has gone out all over the English-speaking world. This new edition has given me the opportunity to make some additions to the text.

The intervening years have confirmed my view that these plants, and their unique qualities, are an essential part of a wholesome diet. Not only are they beneficial to health but their imaginative use raises once more the level of cookery to that of a creative art. It was my endeavour to provide an extract from the existing wealth of material, which for some readers may appear to be of an unusual taste. If, however, it acts as a stimulus to the mental digestion of its contents, and if it is found to be of practical value, then it will have served some purpose, and may even be of help in building the bridge from the past to the future.

I wish to thank Lisa Walters for her kind contribution of the cover design, and Andrew Geuter for his kindness and patience in producing the illustrations of the herbs. No less does my gratitude go to all those friends who have given their generous support, including the printers, in finally producing this new edition.

Maria. Geuter.
Broome Farm, Clent. Michaelmas 1977.

INTRODUCTION

to the 1978 edition.

From ancient times medical practice has been associated with nutrition. Food and remedy were, not so strictly defined as they are today. Each advance in human consciousness has left behind its traces in both spheres, and now food no longer acts as remedy nor does the remedy assist as food.

In the 5th century B.C. the unknown author of the writings of Hippocrates on *Ancient Medicine* had then already described the beginning of a long chain of development in the following way:

"The fact is, that sheer necessity has caused men to seek and to find medicine, because sick men did not, and do not profit by the same regimen as men do in health. To trace the matter yet further back, I hold, that not even the mode of living enjoyed at this present time by men in health would have been discovered had men been satisfied with the same food and drink as satisfy an ox, a horse, and every animal, save man, I mean the raw products of the earth: fruits, leaves and grass. For on these cattle feed and grow and live without distress not needing any other diet. And I believe to begin with man used the same food. Our present ways of living have, I think, been discovered and elaborated during long periods of time. For many and terrible were the sufferings of men from strong and brutish living when they partook of crude foods, uncompounded and possessing strong qualities, the same as men would suffer at the present time..."

At the end of this the writer admits that he had to look for the origin of his medical art in cooking.

These words handed down to us from bygone times are still valid. In the 20th century, in so far as "many and terrible are the sufferings of men when they partake of foods" which have nowadays to be traced back further than the kitchen, to farms, gardens, orchards—to laboratories, food-industry, economic conditions, etc.

In his early state of existence on Earth, man was gifted, as was the animal, with a natural instinct that enabled him to distinguish between good and bad, right and wrong, and this guided him also in the choice of his food. Yet as he advanced to higher faculties, such as intellect and reason, his instinct began to fail and to become unreliable. In order that he might adapt his food to his mental progress he found henceforth the necessary guidance in the dietetical regimen of the physician. It is from such regimen as far as they exist in writing, that we can recapture something of the conception of nature and man, and of the prevailing principles in nutrition during; the classical age.

We find these were based on the four elemental powers of fire, air, water and earth, which were the link between the invisible, ethereal and the visible physical realm of nature. In those times people lived in much closer contact with the elements than they do today. As much as they loved and revered them as their friendly helpers, in the same measure they feared and needed the immense power of destruction of these mighty giants of the North, South, East and West, the rulers of the cold, hot, dry and wet seasons of the year. According to man's good or evil deeds, they would either support and protect him, or they opposed and even destroyed him. He felt himself confronted by elemental actions of which the actors remained unseen behind the curtain of the stage of earthly existence. Only the great Sages of Antiquity, through their exceptional vision, were still able to penetrate into these regions, and it was their insight into the secrets of that world that gave rise to the ancient Greek philosophies.

While Heraclitus saw the sole creative power in the principle of fire, Thales of Milet claimed that the physical world has arisen from the water. Yet on the whole the elemental beings—which in myths and fairy-tales were called gnomes, undines, sylphs and salamanders—were regarded as the ever active hands of the Gods, moulding, shaping, forming and condensing what finally appeared in physical manifestation. Behind the scenes they were engaged in the multitude of mysterious changes that take place in the kingdoms of nature; they collaborated in the perpetual transformation from life to death, from death to rebirth; they were the unceasing builders of the bridge between heaven and earth, between nature and man.

What they did outside in immeasurably great proportions, they did within the human organism in miniature *via* his warmth, gaseous, fluid and solidifying processes, and as they provoked extreme heat and cold in nature so also they induced the rise and fall of the temperature in man. The human temperaments too expressed themselves in their positive and negative behaviour. Therefore a predominating temperament was to be observed in its overpowering influence on a particular part of the organism, and the careful treatment and regulation of the temperamental indisposition was applied as an effective measure in the prevention of illness. Yet on the proper interplay of all four temperaments depended that state of balance, the achievement of which was the essential aim in nutrition, as it was in every other care for human health. Our modern conception of hygiene is restricted to merely physical measures, whereas that of those ancient times had been directed to the whole being of man, to his bodily, soul and spiritual needs. This required all possible assistance that could be derived from the various spheres of culture with the sole aim that man, in his earthly life, should be brought to such a state of harmony and perfection as would satisfy his Creator. Of this Greek culture stands for us as the classical example. In its loftiest sense *Culture* meant the collaboration of man with the Gods, in which the elements were regarded as the indispensable mediators, the highest being the Sacred Fire.

This may shed some light for us on the profound knowledge of that time concerning the elemental world and its ethereal and physical dominion in nature and man. Its tradition was kept alive throughout many centuries. Since the rise of natural science it withdrew into the background waiting to reappear in the garment of the 20th century, at the beginning of a new era.

*   *   *

> *"More servants wait on man*
> *Than he'll take notice of".*
> Emerson — Perpetual Forces.

In all that we do for the production of food in farms and gardens, and for its preparation in the kitchen, we are indeed dependent on these perpetual forces; without their services life would be unthinkable. A spell of fine weather followed by rain will have beneficial effects on the crops; yet when the rain persists, it may cause damage and disaster. By providing the right heat, we can ensure that the bread will rise well; but with a sudden fall of temperature it goes flat, or, as people used to say: "It becomes sad".

It is the same with the human temperaments. In one way or another the prevailing moods leave their mark on the physical constitution. Therefore the treatment of temperamental indispositions should be started as early as possible in childhood. This is partly the task of education, partly of nutrition, and it requires the co-operation of both teachers and parents. Failing that, medical advice may be needed.

In a classroom of children the teacher will be confronted by all four temperaments, and to cope with their peculiarities is no easy task. He needs to know how to deal with the negative side and to bring out the positive aspect of each temperament, so that the rowdy, choleric children will apply their willpower to their lessons and become constructive; the sanguine ones, who tend to be everywhere but in their right place, may be content to sit still for awhile and concentrate on their subject, the phlegmatic children may become active, and the melancholics will want to come out of their seclusion and partake in the life and work they are all sharing. Yet it depends entirely on the skill, understanding and patience of the teacher — and not least upon his own efforts to achieve harmony within himself — whether he can expect to establish harmony among the conflicting temperaments of the pupils in his care.

Dietetical treatment differs from that of education in so far as a predominating temperament needs an opposing element which is able to counteract its superfluous strength. For that very purpose it is essential to study the relationship of the various types of nutritive plants, and moreover their inclination towards the different elements. Thus we can learn in the school of nature that a fruit which ripens in the heat of the sun has an affinity to the choleric, whereas a bean climbing up the pole towards the element of air and light, displays a characteristic of the sanguine temperament. In contrast to this we find that a large cabbage sitting on the ground is indeed a picture of the still, inanimate watery element, and in its underground existence the root obviously reveals the melancholic nature.

From such and many similar observations we shall be able to find the right guidance for our practical work; at any rate they will be of help in selecting and preparing food in such a way that it may act as a support instead of an impediment to our endeavours.

Some of the almost inexhaustible energies of a choleric child may well be used up by means of a diet composed of adequate proportions of the lower parts of the plant, of roots and leaves and in particular of raw salads, and of starch-containing foods, such as wholemeal bread, macaroni, solid puddings, etc., and whatever demands effort in digestion. Thereby much of the surplus energy can be employed in the destruction of matter by the metabolism, energy which might otherwise be exerted in a less desirable way.

The treatment of a sanguine child is far more difficult. Being of a cheerful disposition, he likes to enjoy life, flying from one experience to another and seldom carrying through anything he sets out to do. He will show similar tendencies in the way he eats, which at times will amount to almost nothing, and he seems to exist on air. What he most likes is to indulge in sweet things, giving preference to all that is easily eaten and quickly digested. He resists coming down from his bean-stalk, for he finds it hard to have to get in touch with the salty element of the earth. Yet the counteraction of salt is essential to his mental processes. His digestion must therefore achieve something of the endurance that is needed for the transformation of mineral substances on the long path to their destination, to the head, the nerves and senses. Here, too, roots and leaves will provide the right balance, yet they are made more easily accessible to his peculiar quick digestion in a cooked state. He will, however, always prefer to turn to those elevating forces which take him to the realm where he feels most at home; but there is one thing that can bring him nearer to the phlegmatic nature, something he will hardly ever reject, and that is cream.

The food for the phlegmatic temperament should be made as choleric as possible, so as to encourage the digestion and other organic functions. In this case the forces of the upper elements of warmth and light are most essential. Vegetables that are themselves of a phlegmatic type, such as marrow, cabbage, potato, etc., are less suitable activators than, for instance, spinach, young nettles, sorrel, lettuce, and in general all fresh salads and fruits. A phlegmatic temperament needs to be stirred by a great variety of foods, possibly something different every day, as this will help to prevent it from settling down into a state of stagnation, and from falling back into inactivity.

A melancholic child is apt to retire into his own shell. The symptoms arising from his isolation, his sad look, his moodiness, lack of interest and his rejection, all these are indications of his craving for sweetness. The upper parts of the plants, the sweet aromatic fruits, honey, sugar, are here the remedies. Naturally care must be taken not to go to an extreme; sweet foods should be handled with discrimination, and be regarded as a supplement to the human warmth, love and sympathy, which of course will best induce him to come forth from the darkness of his rooty existence to the sunny and joyful side of life.

We find that a child does not only react to the food as such, but in his own way he reflects something of the negative or positive aspects of the temperament that are predominant in those who prepare the food.

It lies in the very nature of a choleric person to overseason food not only by adding too much salt or pepper, but even more so by anger, impatience, intolerance, and any other such temperamental spices. Yet if these are changed into sunshine, loving attention and good humour, a child will always respond with appreciation of what he will probably call a "super meal", however simple it may be.

A sanguine cook has the inclination to give too much time and effort to her chief interest in making sweet dishes. To her all else is of minor importance, and it will not worry her if other temperaments go short. Her positive side will, however, come out best when, for the sake of those in her care, she is able to forego some of her own satisfaction and thereby she will help children to learn to think of others without having to be reminded.

A phlegmatic cook likes to revel in large and rather tasteless quantities, and as she expects others to do likewise, she dishes out accordingly. Yet she must indeed feel her generosity has failed when much food is left on the plate. From such disappointments she may, however, learn that quality is, after all, as important as quantity, and realising this her cooking will be received with enjoyment and even with the request for more.

In contrast to this, the main tendency of a melancholic person will be towards saving and cutting down in all possible ways. By being *over*-economical certain essential human qualities, which are as much a nourishing factor as the food-substances themselves, are also cut down. In consequence, a feeling of oppression overshadows a meal, and this will, of course, continue in the same manner into the processes of digestion. Children react instinctively to this by helping themselves to food between meals. Thus saving becomes an illusion.

We find that children are almost clairvoyant in perceiving the genuine side of any temperament that has understanding and sympathy for the needs of others; particularly so in the case of a melancholic temperament. Whatever the economic circumstances, compassion and love will always make the best of what there is, so that what to begin with may have seemed to be too little, in the end may turn out to be plenty.

Such observations are helpful too in understanding certain difficulties which children are apt to show with regard to eating. They have indeed the capacity of holding up to us the barometer of our inner weather conditions. If we fail to harmonise these within ourselves, we may inflict as much harm *via* the food, as a teacher who is unable to control his temperament in front of his class.

In the preparation of a meal we ought to be concerned not only with mixing food substances but also with a higher kind of chemistry of ethical components. In fact we begin to revise and widen our usual conception of a menu. Its composition should therefore also embrace the four temperaments, for we have learned that among our cultivated plants we find everything that can satisfy their needs. These plants, however, present only one part of our nourishment, the other part depends on the addition of herbs and spices. They contribute their own essential qualities not only to the choleric, sanguine, phlegmatic and melancholic nature of man but they are closely linked up with the cosmic temperaments which reveal themselves through the four seasons. All the year round, they provide us with their corresponding properties, and in harmonising these with our food substances we are practising a custom that in the English kitchen is so rightly signified as *seasoning*.

Originally most nutritive plants had been cultivated and fostered in a way by which their life-forces were accumulated and strengthened in one particular selected part of the plant, for instance in a root, leaf or fruit, so that they may be adapted to the quantitative and qualitative requirements of the human organism.

Since then a long time has passed by and yet today we still eat:

of the carrot plant.........................only the root;
of the potato plant........................only the tuber;
of the spinach plant......................only the leaf;
of the apple tree ....only the fruit;
of the cereals................................only the seeds.

Such products represent a substantial part of our *outdoor* culture. When they enter the *indoor* culture, the kitchen, the mutual work of man with nature finds its continuation here. We no longer think and work in terms of abstractions but rather do we strive to create a synthesis. This means that we complement one of these single plant organs, for instance the root of the carrot, into a complete organism. And this is to be achieved by means of those accessories which traditionally we designate as condiments.

Apart from salt they are not to be found in the mineral world, nor apart from sugar (honey) in the animal kingdom, but they do exist everywhere in the plant kingdom and comprise all healing and seasoning herbs.

Similar to our cultivated vegetables, they also represent a whole organism consisting of roots, leaves, flowers and fruits, and due to their specific properties, are also adapted to the whole organism of man, to his head, heart and metabolism.

As an illustration we may take a simple example such as the carrot. The carrot has a strong affinity to the human head and is of great support to the functions and development of the nerves and senses, and therefore has a particular place in the diet of a baby. When the time comes to change his diet from milk to solids we begin with fruit juice and cereals, followed by green leaves, spinach, and finally we come down to the roots. Among these the carrot best meets his requirements, for the sun has endowed it not only with a heavenly golden colour but has permeated it with the fruit-quality, with sugar, and for this reason the carrot is signified as a "root-fruit". In this particular case no condiments are needed until the baby is progressing far enough in the development of his senses and when the tendencies towards his temperament begin to appear. This is, of course, different with every child. Yet from then onward an addition of parsley is suitable to complement the root with a leaf-quality, the flower with a little honey, and the seed with some plant-oil. Thus we have made a very simple composition with a minimum of condiments.

In great contrast to the yellow carrot, the preparation of a red cabbage is a very different venture. Observing it in the garden we perceive first of all its dull bluish red colour and then its formation that resembles a rosebud, though of an unusually large almost grotesque size. It looks as if it might be able to copy a rose, but evidently its aim seems to be too high to reach, and as an image of the phlegmatic temperament, it remains sitting with its full weight on a short stump on the ground.

But now when it is to be prepared in the kitchen, herbs and spices come to its aid, each one with its own capacity and characteristics, as is shown in the following two examples, by creating a whole plant organism of condiments:

I		II	
Oil seed	Sunflower oil	Oil seed	Olive oil
Seed	Mustard	Seed	Caraway
Fruit	Sour apple	Fruit	Lemon
Fruit	Rosehip conserve	Flower	Rose elixir
Flower	Clove	Flower	Honey
Stem	Cane sugar	Stem	Angelica candied
Leaf	Levisticum	Leaf	Bay
Bulb	Onion	Bulb	Garlic
Root	Horseradish	Root	Ginger
Mineral substance	Salt	Mineral substance	Salt

When we try to complement the flower of the cabbage we must think of something quite extraordinary which only the rose itself is able to contribute (example II). Thus, with a teaspoonful of rose elixir something is accomplished that no one and nothing else could have achieved. The sanguine temperament of the rose has changed the phlegmatic temperament of the cabbage, and by this unexpected lift-up, its heavy weight has been redeemed and raised into lightness. yet who knows what may have happened when suddenly its

25

dull colour lights up and changes into bright red? It must have been the lemon that has complemented the cabbage with its sunlight and brought about this change. Thus the lucky cabbage has done well, and so have all those who afterwards gathered around the table at dinnertime. Yet how different it would have been if one had merely poured sour vinegar over that head, as is frequently done! This needed to be said to make us more conscious of the versatility of human taste.

The importance of taste should by no means be underestimated for it induces the first stage of digestion and, for good or ill, affects all further processes of the metabolism.

In the classical age, Hippocrates stressed the significance of taste by saying:

"If a musician composed a piece all on one note, it would fail to please. It is the greatest changes and the most varied that please the most. Cooks prepare dishes for men of ingredients that disagree while agreeing, mixing together all sorts of things that are the same and things that are not the same, to be food and drink for men. The notes struck by playing music are sometimes high, sometimes low. The tongue copies music in the distinguishing of things which touch it, the acid, the sweet, the discordant and the concordant. When the tongue is well in tune the concord pleases, but there is pain when the tongue is out of tune".

This makes us aware of another connection between plants and man, for the tongue is the instrument that reacts to all their notes of taste.

From the times of the classical age we have inherited the taste-spectrum of Aristotle that contains:

* Sweet
* fatty
* sharp
* hot
* savoury
* sour
* bitter or salty.

This scale of tastes is of the same order as music is to the ear, or colours to the eye. In the same way as the human soul is affected by a happy or sad melody, by light or dark colours, so too sensations of taste express themselves in acceptance or rejection, in sympathy or antipathy; they do indeed induce either a good or a depressed mood which correspondingly influences the digestive processes and thereby determines not only the physical condition but also that of the soul. We may add that the perception of taste is a much needed stimulation, for it participates in keeping our thinking mobile, active and alive.

While now all the ingredients, including herbs and spices, are passing through the cooking process, based on the elemental forces of fire and water, all outlets will be unlocked and the substances and flavours thus released begin to melt into each other. Finally all the contents have undergone a transformation into a completely new product: a synthesis has come about. What has escaped from it on the wings of the air is immediately taken up by the sense of smell, whereas the actual solid part of the food needs to be touched by the tongue before any taste can be perceived. In any case, these two senses have a great affinity. It smells good! It tastes good! Such exclamations may be heard in the kitchen and they promise a good sound appetite.

Yet in contrast to a healthy appetite we also meet the opposite on all sides. This conveys to us that real interest and enjoyment of food are no longer stimulated, that much is produced, prepared and consumed without the participation of sufficient human thinking and conscience, a shortcoming that gives rise to one of the many physiological as well as psychological deficiencies which nowadays mark the decline of our cultural life. A failing appetite may already be induced when, without much consideration, food products are obtained, the contents of which can hardly be tested correctly without our senses of smell and taste. As long as these senses are not undermined by **chemical substitutes** they may still support our ability to discriminate. Yet this will be prevented evermore inasmuch as, in their earliest years, children are already given food and drink containing substances which are very much to the disadvantage of their sense perception. For many years past we have been exposed to all kinds of such almost inescapable attacks on our well-being and health. May it be by the farmer or gardener who is forced by economical pressure into quantitative production, yet without doubt at the expense of the consumer who bears the depreciation of its qualitative value.

Or we may be informed by our disappointed sense of smell that particular flowers have lost their scent, and instead evil-smelling sprays pollute the air for man, animal and plant alike. Such problems in the field of nutrition are apt to be transformed and to reappear as almost insolvable questions in the field of education. Since they have risen to the surface of our social life, a great versatility of hygienic measures will be required. Among these, herbs will prove to be of vital help in nutrition, for they do not come from subterrestrial regions but with their harmonising and healing properties descend from above, from the world of Sun, Moon and Stars.

Centuries ago, when prominent Herbalists exercised a great influence on human nutrition, the *Essentia condimentum* was valued as the mediator between nutritional plants and their corresponding healing herbs. Now the question is justified: What are we actually doing when we combine Cucumber with Dill, Beans with Savory, potatoes with Horseradish, Cabbage with caraway? We are consciously reestablishing the equivalent state when once upon a time edible plants were blessed with both—with nourishing and healing qualities.

Nowadays when we are facing up to almost insurmountable difficulties in all spheres of life, we are bound to wake up to urgent needs and deeds. To these also belongs the cultivation of herbs. In trying to do justice to their practical application, the following plant sketches have been written and illustrated by drawings. May they contribute something to the recognition that *wholesome* food is the preliminary step to *Healing*.

BAY TREE

Laurus nobilis
Lauraceae

The Laurel or Bay Tree is one of the outstanding features of the Mediterranean landscape, it appears there as a grand and noble figure invested with a solemn mood. In northern districts—due to climate—the growth of this evergreen tree is checked at about 20^{ft}, (6.1^m), whereas in southern regions it can reach a height of 60^{ft}, (18.3^m), carrying a wealth of luxuriant foliage and greenish-yellow flowers.

Its propagation is best done in August by starting young shoots under glass. During the first two years the plant needs careful protection from cold winds and frost, but after being well eslished it is almost weather-resistant. The aromatic leaves may be picked all the year round, and are used in cooking either fresh or dried. The best month for drying is August, having used up the maximum of sun-forces they are then of highest quality.

Sweet Bay, or true Laurel, is easily confused with the Berry Laurel *Prunus lauro cerasus*, a member of the same family, of a similar aroma, but apparently poisonous, and used only in pharmacy.

Amongst the many different species of the *Lauraceae* spread all over the earth, *Laurus nobilis* occupies the throne. Laurus means of high renown. By going into its history we find this confirmed. The French name is *Laurier d'Apollon.*

Greek mythology relates that Apollo took the crown of Wisdom from the Jupiter Tree, the Beech, before it was replaced by the Laurel, the Tree of the Sun. According to Ovid's Metamorphoses, Apollo had fallen in love with Daphne, the daughter of the Arcadian River God, and as he pursued her, Gaea, her mother changed her into a Laurel Tree, and dedicated it to the Gods. Ever since, Daphne, the sweetest melody from the Lyre of Apollo, has been enchanted in that tree, waiting for times to come, when once more her music can be heard by human souls.

In the sacred Laurel Groves that Song of Heaven could still be heard by those who by their wisdom had conquered the powers of darkness in that very realm where the sound of the Sunlight had been silenced. The victorious were crowned with the Laurel wreath as a symbol of the Sun. For a long time the Laurel played its part in the ancient rites and festive ceremonies, yet when they became decadent the Laurel vanished from the altars of the Temples.

It lived on, however, in the medical practice of physicians, and in their writings the tradition was handed down and found its due place in the old Herbals. Apart from its numerous healing qualities, it is interesting to note that it was much used for making the drunken man sober and for restoring his consciousness.

Thus we can trace the path of the Laurel from the lofty heights of the classical age, where it had been offered to the Gods, whereas in medicine and nutrition it was devoted to the physical body—to the Temple of Man.

Today the bay leaf is still famous for its particular flavour in cooking. *It is most effective in food-Products that grow, under the earth, in the dark, and are of a cold nature, such as root vegetables and tubers. The same applies to Fish, meat, game, in fact to all that belongs to the dark side of the food-spectrum. For instance, applied in vinegar, which is much used in salad-dressings and in Preserving, a bay leaf will replace some of the sunshine that it has lost in its transformation from sugar to acidity.*

On the whole the functions of the sweet Laurel are directed to the head, to the processes of nerves and senses, especially to the ear, and to the consciousness. This helps us to form a true picture of its qualities. In bygone times the

Laurel, in a symbolical way, adorned the human head with the Sun. In our times we have become aware of the valuable mineral substances and these, *via* the process of nutrition, in reality crown the head with forces of Light, whereas its Warmth-forces of the aromatic oil offer peace to the mind.

BORAGE

Borago off.
Boragineae

This old saying has undoubtedly arisen from an imaginative conception of this plant, which in our modern view seems antiquated, but nevertheless may bear a spark of truth. In any case the picture of a herb garden would be incomplete without this attractive and most characteristic herb.

Borage prefers light soil, and should be sown in a row in April. At a height of 2^{in}, (5.08^{cm}), the leaves are ready to be picked for use in the kitchen. As they are best when young and tender, it is advisable to make another sowing in July to secure a continuous supply. Where Borage has gone to seed masses of seedlings appear in the following spring, and if some are left to mature, they provide excellent food for bees. It grows up to 2-3^{ft}, (0.3-0.61^{m}), the stem and leaves are succulent, of greyish-green colour, and have a hairy surface. In fact, the whole plant is covered with fine bristles, indicating its strong silicious nature. The leaves give forth a refreshing, cucumber-like aroma, which during a long spell of rain is apt to decline. A special characteristic is the interchange of the sky-blue and pink colouring of its flowers. These with their rich content of nectar are permeated with silicic acid, by similar formative forces to those that in the mineral world shape the hexagonal form of quartz, and in the animal kingdom the cell of the honeycomb. There is no doubt that bees foster a particularly good relationship with this herb, and therefore the bee-keeper also.

Borage has come to Europe from the East. Because of the Arabian name of *Alkanet* for Anchusa, Linné assumed that Borage must have come from Aleppo. But this is a less important point than the great controversy amongst herbalists about the name *Borago* being a corruption of the Latin name *Corago*. This should be its real name. The syllable "*Cor*" has indeed many meanings such as heart, mind, soul, understanding, courage, confidence, and the syllable "*ago*" means to drive, to carry out, to move, to cultivate, all of which are essential qualities of the human Ego. Thus *Corago* refers to the Heart and to the Ego. Borage has a different origin. It is derived from the Italian *Borra*, French *Bourra*, Latin *Burra*, which means woolly and refers to the hairy covering of this plant. By comparing the two names it is obvious that *Corago* describes the qualitative nature of the herb, while *Borago* emphasises an outer characteristic. The latter appeals to our sense-perception and therefore we find it easier to accept the name *Borago*. We have to use our imaginative sense, however, to detect the true spark in both names, and we can do so by ignoring the first letter of the syllables *Cor* and *Bor*, leaving us with *Or*, which means *Aurum*, the Gold of the Sun, the moving spirit of the heart.

According to its diverse application in medicine, Borage is primarily linked up with the circulation of the blood. A compress with a solution of Borage is recognised as a means to relieve congested veins after long hours of standing; thus much can be done to prevent varicose veins. The exhilarating forces of this herb stimulate the organic functions, make the heart feel easy and elevated, light up the consciousness and assist the mind in keeping awake and active, all these conditions being essential to a cheerful mood.

The fresh young leaves are used mainly in salads and cold drinks.

Borage is also of help to farm animals and poultry. It acts as a tonic and if made available to them they will satisfy their need.

Furthermore, the very existence of Borage in the garden is a natural protection to plant life. Its wealth of silicious forces strengthens the resistance of other plants in their battle against diseases and infesting pests.

For all these reasons we may see the truth of the saying:

"A garden without Borage
Is like a heart without courage".

BURNET

Poterium sanguisorbeae
Rosaceae

Burnet is generally regarded as one of the "old-fashioned" herbs. Yet if we try to understand its qualities it may, like so many other things today, become fashionable once again.

There are two kinds of Burnet, and they are easily confused. Burnet major *sanguisorbeae off.* and Burnet minor *Poterium sanguisorbeae*. The latter is the one which is commonly called Salad-Burnet and is used for culinary purposes. Burnet *saxifraga*, or *Pimpinella saxifraga*, is an Umbelliferae and has only medicinal properties.

Burnet may be sown in drills in spring and in succession during the rest of the season. Yet being a perennial it is easily propagated by division of roots. The young leaves can be cut for use in the kitchen at a height of 2^{in}, (5.08^{cm}), and new growth will follow. The leaves burst forth with great vigour as from a spring of fresh water; but in the upper part of the plant this rich flow of life is counteracted by the light from above. The angular stems become almost dry and hard, the round leaves change into lanceolated shape, and become more serrated as they approach the flower. The very unusual flower-head bears no petals, it consists of a cluster of square calyces which bring forth only tiny red pistils in its upper part, while thirty or forty stamens appear in the lower part about a week or two later. Its flowering time begins about mid-summer; the seeds are hard and of a peculiar angular shape. The balance thus produced between the upper and lower parts of the plant is an indication of the harmonious nature of this herb.

The name *Poterium* means drinking-cup or vessel, due to its former great use as an infusion for wine and beer and other drinks, for making the heart easy and merry. Yet there is another reason which justifies this name. This plant is in itself a drinking cup; it has the capacity to imbibe the imperceptible moisture that arises from the earth, and this enables it to preserve its verdure even in the driest weather, when all other vegetation is exhausted.

According to old Herbals, it acts as a styptic, it has drying and astringent qualities and was regarded as an important wound healer. From this had arisen the name *Bloodwort*, or *Ironwort*. It was especially dedicated to the function of the liver, which is indeed the drinking cup within the human organism and which is very much dominated by thirst. Burnet, however, releases the heart from having to carry the burden of excessive liquid, and this is the real reason why it was used so much in alcoholic drinks. ***Its use in the kitchen is similar to that of Borage, the two herbs seem to complement each other.***

Some herbalists felt inclined to call it Peponella or Pompion, because of its affinity to the flavour of cucumber. The cucumber is of a highly watery consistency, and for this reason it was looked upon as a plant of the Moon. As one of the oldest cultivated vegetables it played a great part in those times when *Jehovah* was the Moon-Deity of the Hebrews. From the East seems to have come the name cowcumber; there the cow is still revered as a holy animal of the Moon, and the cowcumber was one of the sacred lunar plants.

We can, of course, observe the lunar nature of the cucurbitaceous plants also in other characteristics. The flesh and flavour of the edible fruits of this family differ in the various members, and most of them are dependent on a high degree of warmth and moisture. A pumpkin, for example, may develop into a monstrous plant covering an eighth of an acre and producing massive, head-shaped fruits. It presents us with a picture of a large prickly animal- like plant, crawling over the ground, carrying its many heads, and stretching out its tendrils, reminding us of prehistoric conditions, before the earth had become solid. It is a reminiscence of an intermediate state in which animal and plant were not differentiated, as they did become in a later state of evolution. Yet they still seem to be floating in water, of which their hard skin holds up to 95 per cent. From that point of view the cucumber too may be regarded as a drinking cup and also rightly called *poterium*. In fact, in some countries the particularly solid skins of some varieties are preserved and turned into spoons, bowls, cups and dishes, or are much used as vessels for drawing and storing water.

Because of the predominating element of water, some fruits, such as marrow and pumpkin, have not been endowed with much flavour, they are lacking in stimulating qualities, and amongst the fruits represent the phlegmatic temperament. In contrast to this one-sidedness we find a herb such as Burnet is harmonised within itself with regard to the elements, as we can see from its angular seeds and stems, its absorption of water, its lightness in the upper part of the plant and the concealed fire of its flower. Such complete balance is a special characteristic of the Rose family and we can understand why Burnet was considered a special favourite of the Sun.

The combination of Cucumber and Burnet provides us with an illuminating example of how Moon-forces and Sun-forces can be brought into harmony; thus we may learn of yet another aspect in balancing our food in a way that best suits the human organism.

TARRAGON

Artemisia dracunculus
Compositeae

Of the two kinds of Tarragon grown in this country, the French variety, a native of the Mediterranean countries, is superior in quality, but in cultivation it is less adaptable to our climate than the Siberian or Russian variety.

Tarragon is a perennial herb which is almost a shrub in habit. The woody stems divide into numerous branches, carrying plain, long, spear-shaped leaves, and from July to August it bears inconspicuous greenish flowers. The seeds do not ripen in this country and the supply depends on imports; propagation is mostly done by division. The creeping roots are very vigorous, almost like those of couchgrass; they are easily divided and do best in light, well drained soil. For drying, the leaves should be cut before the flowers develop, and once more in early September.

This herb is an exceptional source of warmth-forces and its aroma gives an interesting flavour to all kinds of fresh salads, such as lettuce, endive, cabbage, cucumber, tomato, as well as to salads prepared from cooked vegetables, e.g. celeriac, carrots, beetroots, etc. Tarragon vinegar of course is still much used in *salad-dressings and for preserving*, but to have the full benefit of the qualities of this herb it is better to use it fresh, as long as it is in season.

Tarragon is a member of the large family of the Compositeae, and belongs to a special group of aromatic herbs, the Artemisias. These are outstanding with regard to their

38

volatile oil of a bitter aroma. Its chief representative is the herb commonly called Wormwood *Artemisia absinthium*, in which the extraordinary warming qualities and the bitter flavour form a synthesis that is of special encouragement to the digestive processes, it activates the liver and gallbladder, raises vitality and in general strengthens resistance to illness. It is not applied in food, rather it builds the bridge from the bitter pole of the scale of tastes to the realm of medicine.

Among the 200 different varieties of Artemisias, Tarragon (*Artmisia dracunculus*) is of a much simpler form, not only outwardly but its flavour too is milder, and in general it seems to be modified in its qualities, and therefore it is suitable for culinary use.

There has been some controversy as to whether the herb Wormwood should not better be called Warmwood. Yet in the Latin name *Artemisia*, we find the confirmation that Wormwood must be right. This group of herbs was dedicated by the ancient Greeks to Artemisia, the Goddess of Nature, who according to mythological tradition was the twin sister of Apollo. Armed with bow and arrow she brought death to mortals, and punished offences against herself and morality. But she brought also healing and renewal of life and, like her brother Apollo, she too was engaged in combat with the serpent, Python, who lay coiled in the realm of darkness.

In Greek, Tarragon is called *Drakon*, hence the German name *Dragon*. It is for good reasons that Tarragon is still used in combination with vinegar. Although vinegar had its part to play in human development—since it directs man's consciousness to the earth—yet it conceals within itself that peculiar force of which people in the past used to say: "It eats up the blood". But in its insignificant outer appearance, *Artemisia dracunculus* stands there with its cosmic bow and arrow of warmth and light in the conquest of the powers of darkness, the Python-forces, *i.e.* the poison in our present day food.

ANISE

Pimpinella anisum
Umbelliferae

As one of the oldest oriental remedies and spices, Anise found its way into the English herb gardens as early as the 14th century. But our moist climate makes it difficult for the seeds to ripen and it is easier to import them from warmer and drier countries. It can be grown success-fully in warm sheltered places and during a long dry spell the seeds will mature. Because germination takes from 25 to 30 days, sowing must be done as early as possible under glass, and after the late frosts, in May, the plants may be transferred to a sheltered border of well-composted light soil.

The delicate, slender tap-root bears a tall upright stem, 3-4[ft], (1-1.22[m]), in height, which, as it develops, forms several side branches. The foliage undergoes a remarkable change from round to heart-shaped leaves, divided into three, which be-come deeply cut and serrated higher up and finally, near to the flower, appear in a simple, linear form. The delicate light umbels bear tiny white flowers from July onward and with any luck the greyish-brown seeds are ripe in September. As with all Umbelliferae, the best seeds are taken from the main umbel, which matures first. Their fertility lasts for 2-3 years.

The whole plant is highly aromatic and its healing prop-erties are mainly effective for the digestive and excreptional functions. It was one of the famous old home remedies, and the tradition of its **use in baking** is still carried on in the kitchen. But it is no less helpful in **cooking vegetables, par-ticularly those of the brassica type and of roots.** As with so many herbs, it is liked by some and disliked by others, yet by making a solution from the seeds and adding this to the cooking process, its flavour should hardly be noticed. Anise is also a favourite spice **in pickled fruits and chutneys.** It gives a pleasant flavour to otherwise **tasteless jam, and it makes stewed pears and quinces easier to digest.** A strong cup of **Anise-tea** is of great comfort and relief to coughs and colds and to digestive troubles. **Warm milk and honey mixed with Anise-tea** and given before bedtime is a soothing drink for restless children.

This herb has indeed a special affinity to the nursery. It encourages the secretion of milk in the nursing mother, and its carminative and quietening quality seems to have been specially given by nature to suit the baby. But it does not cease there, it is still required during the time when solid food is introduced and then a small dose of Anise-powder is helpful to the digestion of starch, in biscuits, rusks and bread as well as in vegetables.

Thus the character of Anise may be pictured rightly as the good fairy Pimpinella, who at the birth of the human being stands at the cradle tending the needs of the newcomer to the earth, a truth which in so simple and beautiful a way is expressed in the saying:

> *"With Pimpinel-sweet Pimpinel*
> *Mother and Babe are doing well".*

FENNEL

Foeniculum off.
Umbelliferae

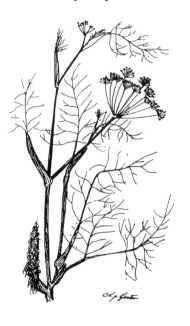

These words from Longfellow's "Goblet of Life" give an indication of the great figure and character of Fennel a midst the more delicate members of its family. Although it likes to occupy a sunny position in the herb garden, it will grow well in any soil and develop into a magnificent plant.

The roots descend deeply into the soil and its tubular hollow stems send forth an abundance of feathery foliage which, under the influence of light, has almost lost its character as a leaf; only the tender ribs have remained. This strong action of division proceeds further, right up into the flower head; there numbers of flower-stalks divide once more into small umbels—the actual bearers of the tiny yellow florets—and together make up the large one. The whole plant is permeated by a sweet pleasant aroma. Being perennial, a matured plant will after a couple of years produce an enormous amount of seed. According to the season they ripen during September and October, and their germination capacity lasts for 2–3 years. A succession of young tender leaves for culinary use is best obtained by making a new sowing in early summer, before the matured plants go to seed. The leaves are unsuitable for drying.

There is another variety called Bronze or Indian Fennel, with the same flavour, and of a warm, reddish-brown colour, and in interesting contrast to the green variety.

Florence Fennel, or *Finnochio, Foeniculum dulce*, is less known in this country, but is much in demand in Italy, France and other European countries as a vegetable of a very fine, rather sweetish flavour and of a wholesome quality. Its cultivation demands well-composted soil and, being a delicate annual, it is best sown after the frosts have passed. On the whole it is of much smaller size than the perennial Fennel, for the simple reason that its vitality is drawn downwards; it accumulates its nourishing qualities at the base of the stem and, like celery, it needs earthing up for blanching. This tender edible part of the plant is much recommended for *special diets, for patients, babies and old people.*

Fennel is a very old and faithful companion of mankind and its history is said to reach as far back as the creation of man. Ancient Greek mythology relates that *Prometheus* and his brother *Epimetheus* were entrusted with the task of creating Man on earth and of providing him and the animals with the faculties necessary for their existence. But *Epimetheus* expended all his gifts on the animals and had nothing left for man. So *Prometheus* went up to Heaven and, concealing in a hollow fennel-stalk the fire of the Sun, he brought it down to earth. Man, being now in possession of this gift, was more than a match for all the animals.

Pliny praised this herb for strengthening and restoring the eyesight, so that the eye might shine upon Nature with the clearness and brightness of the sunlight and in every detail perceive the Creation of God.

Among the old-fashioned home remedies, Fennel was regarded as an aid to digestion, having remarkable carminative properties and encouraging excretion. It is well known for its comforting and loosening effects in bronchial catarrhs and coughs, for its stimulation of glandular secretions, and for its calming influence on the nerves. Its ancient name of Marathon means to grow thin and slender—as the Fennel does— and this indicates also its slimming effect. Like Anise it has a special place in the nursery. It was an old custom that the midwife washed the eyes of the new-born baby with fennel water to make its sight clear, and to enable it to see the world into which it had entered. **Fennel-tea** is made by boiling a teaspoonful of seeds in water for 5–10 minutes; plain or mixed with milk it helps the baby to bring up wind and to go to sleep. Also it brings down the weight of an overfed baby.

Like Aniseed it should be used in small quantities for *baking biscuits and rusks*. It is helpful to infants and people with a delicate stomach, as it assists the digestion of carbohydrates. *The fresh leaves are used in herb sauces and in salads*, to which the little yellow umbels, together with some blue and pink Borage flowers add a delightful decoration which satisfies the eye also.

In the past, when fresh vegetables were scarce, Fennel was one of the first welcome greens in spring, and was much more in common use. At the seaside, sailors and fishermen believed that, during the time when the Sun enters into Pisces, fish was unwholesome food unless it had the Fennel to give it the blessing of the Sun. Today much of our nourishment consists of unwholesome food, and all the more do we need the blessing of the sun-forces of the Fennel.

ANGELICA

Archangelica off.
Umbelliferae

In great contrast to Fennel or Dill, with their dissipated, airy and feathery foliage, Angelica builds up a handsome, imposing structure, often to a height of 8ft, (2.44m). Based on a strong and firm root system, the luted stalks send forth broad, vivid green serrated leaves. The large umbels of greenish-yellow colour, flower from June onwards, and the seeds ripen in August, but generally retain their fertility for one year only. As germination is slow and capricious, it is best to sow immediately after harvesting, and the seedlings will come up at the end of September. Angelica depends on sufficient moisture, but is adaptable to any kind of soil. The whole plant, from root to seed, is permeated by an aroma that is regarded as the most exquisite of all that the umbelliferous herbs are able to produce. Its medicinal properties are unique in so far as they are effective in all parts of the organism, as to nerves and senses, to respiration and circulation and to the functions of the digestive and glandular systems.

Today its use in the kitchen has almost ceased, except that the candied stems still appear in the traditional **Christmas cake and confectionery.** However, with a renewed interest in this herb we shall find that it can be made use of in many ways. *Its tender leaves together with other fresh herbs are an interesting addition to spring salads; the fresh or candied stems give flavour to stewed fruits or preserves* that have not much aroma of their own. It is especially good in **iced drinks or ice cream**, as it prevents the stomach from getting chilled, and is extremely suitable for sick people.

45

The strong element of warmth enables this herb to withstand even the severe climate of the northern hemisphere as far as Iceland, Norway, Lapland and Siberia, where it is indispensable in the monotonous vitamin-deficient diet of the peoples. The stems are blanched and eaten with bread and butter, and their bread, mostly made of rye, is made more digestible by an addition of the dried and ground roots of Angelica.

Although Angelica is one of the ancient companions of human culture, we learn that its healing qualities were first discovered by an old monk during the Middle Ages. Hence it was planted in the herb-gardens of the monasteries. They supplied, to a great extent, the remedies for the sick, and during the plagues the stalks of Angelica were given to the people to chew as a safeguard against infection. Because of its power of protection from disease this herb was called *Angelica*, the Guardian Angel. The actual healing, however, was due to one of still higher rank in the angelic world, to the Archangel Raphael, thus the Latin name *Archangelica*. Those who had preserved traditional knowledge knew of the special relation of its root to the various functions connected with the head, that realm in which is engaged the highest faculty of man, his thinking; and it was in that very realm of his spiritual being where in reality fear could be overcome. For that reason the root was dedicated to the Holy Spirit and was named *Spiritus sancti radix*, the root of the Holy Ghost.

Today fear is accumulating around us from many sources, and is prevailing in the mind of man. If we turn to nature we find the Angelica is still occupying its cardinal place in the herb garden, and with its own superior forces will once more strengthen the resistance of the human organism. We can learn something of the utmost importance for our present day life, that it is the power of the human spirit which is actually able to conquer fear by collaborating in his active, creative and positive thinking with the Healing Spirit behind the events of our time.

LOVAGE

Levisticum off.
Umbelliferae

Wild Lovage has its home in the mountains of Persia, whereas the common garden Lovage, *Levisticum off.*, came to Europe from the Mediterranean countries where it is found on the hills and mountain slopes at a height of over 2,000^{ft}, (609.6^{m}), a sign that it is specially receptive to the air and the light of such altitudes. This perennial herb loves moist and well composted soil. The massive tough root divides into several thick branches which enter deeply into the ground. It is mainly propagated by division in the spring. The luxuriant foliage expands towards the light, opening out into many triangular, spear-shaped and serrated leaflets of a splendid green colour, but slightly softened by a golden tone. As the stems grow higher, the leaves diminish and finally give way to the pale, greenish-yellow flower-umbels, which appear from June onwards. The seeds ripen during August and should be sown soon after harvesting, as their germination forces seem to last only for one season. After the foliage has died down in autumn the plant gathers all its strength into the root and comes up with new energy in the spring.

All parts of this herb give forth a strong and interesting aroma, which is very like that of Celery, yet it creates the impression that in this plant, cosmic chemistry has produced a compound of special quality. This is confirmed by the fact that it had been designated "the great *Culinarius*", and it deserves this name, for its character is unique. Its sanguine nature is strongly supported by its absorption of light and warmth and therefore has a counteracting influence on the phlegmatic temperament. It is highly recommended for use in *special diet* as a suitable substitute for hot spices, it restores appetite and lost interest in life. In northern regions where fresh vegetables are scarce, the roots are used for food, and the stems are chewed as a preventive of infection, To the modern palate the strong flavour of the root would probably cause an unpleasant sensation, and therefore it should be used as a condiment. For this purpose the roots are cleaned, split in half and strung up and dried in the air. They are then ground into powder and kept in an airtight container to preserve the aroma. This is an excellent flavour for use **in soups, sauces, gravies, stews and for meat and fish**; it helps to bring about a distinctive quality that marks classical cookery.

Like Celery, the stems are suitable for blanching and are eaten with salt. The fresh leaves give an interesting wholesome flavour to salad dressings, to sandwich spreads, herb sauces and to cooked vegetables and pulses. The dried leaves serve the same purposes in winter or can be used all the year round.

The common name Lovage, in German *Liebstoeckle*, in Dutch *Lavas Kruid*, is obviously referring to love. There was a great king who thought that all culture proceeded from the stomach, and many other great people shared that view. But there is yet another saying, which is still in common use today, that the way to a man's heart is reached *via* his stomach. Whoever is convinced of this should indeed make the best use of the great *Culinarius*, of Lovage.

DILL

Anethum graveolens
Umbelliferae

"A salad made with Dill
Is like a man of good will".

The truth of this saying needs to be unravelled as we try to consider a herb which, in its appearance, is similar to Fennel, but altogether much smaller and simpler. It is an annual, grows up to 3^{ft}, (0.91^m), in height and hardly ever produces more than one stem, carrying the very finest, segmented leaves, and umbels of tiny yellow florets. Their petals are slightly turned inward, as though enclosing something of special value.

Because germination takes 20–28 days, the seeds need to be sown as early as possible in March. A good supply of leaves and of seeds is achieved by sowing two rows, one kept for using the young leaves which may be cut during spring, and the other should be thinned out for the plants to mature, to produce seeds. Depending on an early start, the flowering time begins in July and extends into August; then if weather permits, the seeds may be gathered in September. They retain their fertility for 2–3 years.

Although it is greatly reduced in structure, outwardly Dill shows a great resemblance to Fennel, being equally given up to the elements of air, light, warmth, but it surpasses Fennel in warmth, and the aroma is of a greater stimulating and awakening quality and more down to earth. It appeals strongly to the digestive glands which by the very smell of this herb become active, with the result of creating an acute appetite. Its healing properties are similar to those of Fennel, and as to its culinary value, **the fresh leaves, the flowers**

49

and the seeds are suitable to counteract the cold and watery nature of food. For this reason on the Continent large quantities of cucumbers go into food-industry to be pickled with salt and Dill, a most popular stimulant, for it lights up the brain and fires the will.

In the past Dill was known as a herb which, if taken in excess, would cause weakness of sight. Presumably by this is meant that *"second sight"* which for a long time had prevailed as the last remnants of a former vision of the elemental world and had declined into the apprehension of devils, demons, witches and evil powers. Like a flash of lightning the ethereal oil rises to the head, awakens consciousness and overcomes the dulling effects of the oppressing atmosphere in hot summer days. There existed an old custom of burning Dill to drive away thunderous clouds and to clear the air of its sulphurous vapours.

This rather reminds us of the battle that, during autumn, takes place in nature and which marks the Christian festival of Michaelmas, the great fight of St. Michael with the Dragon. For special reasons it is still observed by country people in connection with the Harvest-festival, and it still has a place in the calendar, but its inner content has almost escaped our consciousness. We may be unaware of it, yet the human soul is still involved in this battle—as it always has been—in so far as it witnesses the life-forces in nature giving way to the powers of death. It is that time when the elements take away all that returns to life in the following spring. It is often in the face of death that man becomes aware of his higher, eternal being which does not succumb to earthly laws, and if he has become conscious of this he will indeed have taken part in the victory of the Archangel St. Michael.

Even in the human organism itself a similar battle takes place in a minute way between the sulphur and iron processes of the blood. And we find that the delicate little herb Dill, with its own power of iron and the strength to drive off thunderous clouds, exists in the plant world and acts as one of the unrecognised hosts of the cosmic warrior St. Michael. With all that in mind we are able to see this herb in its right light, and we may conclude that each one of its tiny golden florets with its petals turned inward is but a shield for a spark of cosmic will. In that sense we may understand the saying:

"A salad made with Dill
Is like a man of good will".

CARAWAY

Carum carvi
Umbelliferae

Caraway seeds are easily obtained from our shops and are therefore not much grown in the garden. But there is a great difference in the aroma of seeds which are new and home-produced from those of the commercially grown ones, which may be years old.

This umbelliferous herb is biennial and it is usually sown in August. Germination takes place after 20–30 days, and in the course of autumn the finely serrated leaves develop in the form of a rosette. The whitish root is in shape and aroma similar to a carrot. With new growth in spring, a single stem shoots up to 1 ½^{ft}, (0.46^m), in height, with a number of side branches, all of which bear umbels during June and July, extending into many tiny umbels with masses of white, or sometimes pink, florets. The seeds, shaped like a moon-sickle, ripen in August, and should be sown soon after harvesting. They remain fertile for two years.

The aroma is stronger and warmer than that of Anise or Fennel, and the therapeutic qualities are similar to these in so far as they assist digestive functions, the activity of the glands, and are carminative and diuretic; the leaves and the roots have a corresponding effect.

With cultivation the roots become larger and better in flavour, and are suitable to be cooked and are a welcome supplement to *special diet*, whereas **the young leaves are prepared like spinach or used in fresh salads, herb sauces and soups.** Loyal to tradition, the seeds are still eaten in *seed-cake or in bread.* On the Continent they are much used in **cooking cabbage and roots, and as a spice to soft and solid cheeses, and indeed for anything that needs to be up-lifted by the element of warmth.** Any prejudice against Caraway in food may be overcome if it is applied as an extract from the seeds and this may be added during the cooking process of **vegetables, potatoes, gravies, soups and to numbers of meat-dishes** in which onions are used. Its quality is, however, best retained in the form of freshly ground powder, yet its flavour should not be dominant.

The name *Carum* seems to have been derived from Caria —a district in Asia Minor, rich in aromatic herbs. Yet Caraway conveys a little more of its character if it is understood in the sense of the word "*care*". It is best pictured as a kind and loving caretaker who looks after the house, unlocks the doors of the glands, climbs right to the top and kindles the light in the brain, cleans the windows of the eyes to give a better view of the world, ventilates the rooms, burning any fuel however wet and cold. It also regulates the water system, cares for the comfort of the organism, and is altogether like a good old factotum, devoting his life entirely to the service of his master who, having learned to appreciate his faculties, would not like to be without him.

CORIANDER

Coriandrum sativum
Umbelliferae

This member of the Umbelliferae is a hardy annual which is of slow germination and should be sown early in spring. It is modest in regard to its soil requirements, but likes a sunny position, and seems to do better in the company of other herbs such as Dill, Chervil and Fennel.

The stems are very slender and erect; the leaves broad and deeply cut, while the upper leaves change into numerous segments and, towards the flower, become fine and rigid. The umbels carry tiny white, mauve, or pale pinkish flowers during June and July, and the globular seeds ripen during August, keeping their fertility for 4–5 years.

The outstanding characteristic of this herb is the strongly repulsive smell of the leaves on the one hand, and on the other the pleasing, hot aroma of the ripe seed. It is one of the umbelliferous herbs that tend to be poisonous, and if used to excess it produces a narcotic effect.

In contrast to the leaves, the seeds have a stimulating aromatic quality and are often used as a disguise in medicines. They are carminative and a help to the digestion, particularly of carbohydrates; in consequence, they have been much used in **bread and cakes.** In the old days the seeds were roasted and coated with sugar for children to eat as comfits. In general cooking, Coriander represents one of the chief spices **for meat, fish and stews, also in pickling and preserving fruits.**

Since ancient times Coriander has come to us *via* the eastern trade routes. It had its task in the culture of Egypt, in the classical medicine of Greece, and played a great part in the nutrition and medicine of the Arabs. The Hebrews favoured it as one of the bitter herbs at the Feast of the Passover. It is mentioned in Talmudic writings, while in India it is still an essential ingredient of curry.

The name Coriander is derived from the Greek *Koris*, which means bug. This meaning is expressed in the German name *Wanzenkraut*, meaning Bug-herb, for the repulsive odour of its leaves, and when the seeds are ripening in summer the whole plant appears to be covered with swarms of insects. Being of such an offensive nature, the leaves were considered as a preventive of infesting pests. For this reason they should be grown in the garden and field, and affected crops sprayed with a solution of the leaves instead of using harmful insecticides.

In cooking, only the seed should be used. Although the seed has taken on the outer appearance of a bug, inwardly the aromatic oil has conquered the irritating nature of the leaf, and has acquired the capacity to overcome bad temper or the "lousy mood". A cordial spiced with Coriander has in its very essence the power to bring about this transformation within the human organism, and the same happens when we use this spice in cooking; in other words it re-establishes harmony between the functions of blood and nerves and therefore cheers up and satisfies heart and mind.

CHERVIL

Anthriscus cerefolium
Umbelliferae

None of the old-fashioned herb gardens would have been complete without the company of the cheerful Chervil. Yet today it is hardly known, and its use in the kitchen has almost ceased.

This biennial herb will grow in any soil and is easily raised from seed. The first sowing can be made in March, in a shady place. It will germinate after 10-14 days, but is unsuitable for transplanting, as it will fail to grow proper foliage and will quickly go to seed. After 4-6 weeks it is ready for cutting. Another sowing is recommended for autumn and early spring use, as this is a plant that will stand the winter.

The slender stems grow up to 1-1 ½ᶠᵗ, (0.3-0.46ᵐ), carrying lovely graceful leaves of a bright yellowish-green which turn a delicate pinkish-red when exposed to the sun. The leafstalks are long at the base and bear smaller leaves, growing shorter near the flower. The small white umbels are a picture of levity and seem, in their delicacy, almost to disperse into the air. Their shining black seeds are mostly ripe in August, and remain fertile for 3-4 years.

The therapeutic qualities of Chervil are diuretic and assist in purifying the blood. It has a dissolving effect in rheumatic tendencies or gout, and it disperses congealed blood in bruises, haemorrhoids, or congestion in the breast of a nursing mother. In general, it is of real assistance for the "spring cleaning" of the organism.

There exists another variety of Chervil, *Chaerophyllum bulbosum*, with an edible root which, like the parsley root, can be used in cooking, though rather as a condiment than as a vegetable.

The leaves of Chervil, Anthriscus cerefolium, have a sweetish scent, but a savoury, herbal taste; this variety is more suitable *for use as a fresh herb to give an interesting flavour to salads, herb sauces, sandwich spreads, cheese and to soups* that will stimulate a tired mind. On the Continent, Chervil soup, of light green colour, is a special dish eaten on Holy Thursday. The chopped leaves should be added just before serving, to preserve the aroma.

Once we get used to this herb, we shall find that it brings a breath of fresh air to our food just when we need it most. It has great rejuvenating qualities, cheering up the low constitution and is helpful for those who suffer from the effects of the common winter maladies.

Garden Chervil was at one time given the name of Myrrhis minor, not to be mistaken for Sweet Cicely, *Myrrhis odorata or Myrrhis major.* Chervil was called *Myrrhis* for its volatile oil which has a similar aroma to the resinous substance of Myrrh. The holy Myrrh had been one of the offerings of the Magi at the Event of Bethlehem; that very substance which represented the symbol of death, yet concealed within itself the powers of resurrection and new life.

Thus Chervil with its reviving qualities has its due share in creating the rejoicing mood of the Easter Festival.

PARSLEY

Apium hortense
Petroselinum sativum
Umbelliferae

Parsley is the most favoured and most generally used herb in the kitchen. It is so well known that it needs no description. This refers to the commonly grown, curled garden Parsley, *Apium hortense.*

In this country the plain-leafed, or French Parsley, *Petroselinum sativum*, has retired into the background, partly because it is often mistaken for Fool's or Dog's Parsley, *Aethusa cynapium*, which is poisonous.

In Continental cooking *Petroselinum* is one of the indispensable soup herbs-*Suppenkraut* in German, *Soep Kruid* in Dutch, and *l'Herbe Potage* in French. In these countries they are sold together with celery leaves, young leeks and carrots in small bunches.

Neapolitan or celery-leafed Parsley is cultivated for the sake of its blanched stems and is eaten with salt. There is also a Parsley root, listed in seed catalogues under the name of Hamburg or Turnip-rooted Parsley.

Parsley takes from 4 to 6 weeks to germinate. It requires good soil and Likes to grow in association with or following leguminous crops. To ensure a good supply all the year round, two sowings are recommended: in spring and late summer. In cold districts protection is needed during the winter. In the second year the umbels carry a profusion of delicate, greenish-yellow florets, followed by an abundance of seeds, which ripen during September and keep fertile for up to 5 years.

The whole plant gives forth a strong, stimulating herbal aroma. Being much hardier and nearer to its original state, French Parsley has a still stronger flavour than the curled variety and is more suitable for use in cooking, whereas the latter is better used fresh—and, of course, its decorative leaves are indispensable for garnishing.

Compared with other root vegetables, Hamburg Parsley plays a minor part; nevertheless, it brings its essential root-forces and its own particular flavour to **vegetable soups, stews, pulses and vegetable salads.** *A sauce* made of a finely-grated Hamburg Parsley root mixed with salt, pepper, lemon, oil or cream and a few chopped leaves of curled Parsley to give some colour, goes well **with cold meats, fish, hard-boiled eggs or cheese**, and it also makes an appetising **sandwich spread**.

The qualities of Parsley are manifold, they stimulate the functions of the kidneys, prevent stones and promote excretion, they assist the digestion, encourage the circulation, and its mineral substances make the nerves strong as a rock, therefore the saying, "Eat Parsley and you won't lose your nerve".

During the classical age this herb was highly valued; it played its part in temple ceremonies and in rituals for the dead. Greek mythology relates that it sprang forth from the blood of a Greek Hero, *Archemorus*, the fore- runner of death. As a symbol of Herculean strength it adorned those who were fearless of death, and it crowned the victorious in spiritual conquest; above all, it was dedicated to *Persephone*, or *Core*, the heart and soul of the Earth, who spent half the year in the Netherworld and the other half with *Demeter*, her mother, in the upper regions. It accompanied *Persephone* into the darkness of *Hades*, and it was the key to the gate of the other side of the world. *Petroselinum* means the "Rock" and it was dedicated to St. Peter who was called the Rock and guarded the Key to Heaven.

Thus Parsley has gone with Man through all changing conditions into ever darker realms of life on earth. For some inexplicable reason he has held on to it, even at a time when most herbs are vanishing from his consciousness, while he is going through the gloom and dangers of his self-created underworld. If he emerges from this Hades of our Age, however, and he becomes aware of the fact that there is yet another side to this world, he will not fail to realise that during the dark spell he has clung in his nourishment to one particular herb as to a rock. In the depths of his heart he knew that he was not to lose the key to the gate which leads into the very sanctuary of the human organism, where the Mystery of transformation of matter into spirit takes place.

CELERY

Apium graveolens
Umbelliferae

Celery has a double function, it is used as a vegetable and also as a culinary herb.

Although it is hardly considered these days as a member of the herb garden, wild Celery or Smallage, *Apium graveolens*, is a biennial which is to be recognised by its strong aroma resembling that of garden Celery. It is the original of the cultivated varieties and had been used as a herb long before the latter came into general use. Its cultivation is similar to that of Parsley.

The slender stems carry delicate leaves of intense green, and in the second year, during June and July, masses of white flowers develop and produce an abundance of seeds. It contains about 20 per cent of Natrium and its salty nature is much enhanced by a moist climate and in wet weather. This and its rich iron content are a valuable source of energy for the blood and nerves. It has preserved something of its original forces, which in garden Celery have become weakened in the process of over-cultivation and breeding.

The blanched stems of Celery are mainly eaten raw with salt but they are also used as a cooked vegetable and can be prepared in various ways.

Because of its strong flavour, Celeriac or turnip-rooted Celery, *Apium rapaceum*, is less appreciated by itself as a vegetable but it enriches the taste and quality of **vegetable salads, stews and soups. Cooked and cut in slices and fried in a batter as fritters** it is a welcome change in the monotonous diet during the winter season. It may also be prepared in the same way as horse-radish sauce, cooked or raw, which is excellent with cold meat or as a sandwich spread. Celeriac having an affinity to the reproductive organism is less suitable for children, they mostly show a natural dislike of it, while the upper parts of the plant are more easily accepted. All parts of the Celery plant are edible, root, stem, leaves and seed, which is exceptional amongst other vegetables. The roots are rich in minerals, the leaves and stems are of nutritive quality, and the seeds with their aromatic oil are a stimulant to digestion. Like Parsley this plant can be applied in so many ways, that it is best left to the cook to make wise use of it.

In pre-Christian times, Celery had been one of the herbs in the Sanctuaries and Temples, the roots having been dedicated to *Apium*, the God of the Underworld, who ruled in the dark, salty, subterrestrial regions, where death and mourning prevailed. Yet the upper part was revered as the symbol of the all-renewing life of the Light of the Sun.

If we look at the root of Celeriac—covered all over as it is with a tangled mass of secondary roots—it presents us with a striking image of the head of an old man, and if against this we see the delicate tender Anise plant, the baby of the family, we become aware of the fact that nature has provided the umbelliferous herbs with forces that suit all stages of life, from babyhood to old age.

BALM

Melissa off.
Lobiatae

Amidst the dark needle-leafed Labiatae such as Hyssop, Savory, Thyme and Rosemary, the youthful sanguine nature of Balm appears full of energy, life and cheer, a contrast that is comparable to that of a birch among the solemn coniferous trees. It is a perennial that dies in autumn, and in spring comes up with great vigour. Its square stems carry bright green heart-shaped and finely serrated leaves of a refreshing and enlivening aroma. This is at its best before the flowers develop, and if required for drying should be gathered on a fine day at noon. As soon  as this herb opens its tiny white, rather insignificant flowers, it arouses the interest of the bees, and soon resembles a bee swarm without its hive. The seeds ripen during September and remain fertile for 1–3 years. It is commonly propagated by division of roots, but stronger plants are derived from seed. With the help of some compost it will flourish in any soil in a sunny position.

Originally Balm came from Asia *via* the Mediterranean to Europe. *Pliny* favoured it as a remedy for Hypochondria, for disorders due to the melancholic temperament, and for nervous complaints. The scholastic orders of the Benedictines and Cistertians treasured it as a source of energy for their mental faculties and so did the old herbalists regard Balm as a Sovereign of the brain. It was highly recommended for students suffering from the strain of learning, for its aromatic quality has the power to drive off heaviness of mind, to sharpen understanding and to strengthen the memory. No less has it been valued for its effect on the circulation. It frees the heart from depression, induces a joyful mood and raises the spirit; and since it was also of great assistance to the functions of the metabolism, Balm has been regarded as the "*Doctor Universalis*" among the herbs.

From this we may conclude that we shall benefit much from the properties of this herb which indeed meet a great need of our time. It is used in many ways, for **sandwich spreads, salad dressings, for soups and vegetables.** Balm leaves steeped in water with lemon juice and honey make an **ideal drink** for spring and summer. The dried leaves are used in winter for cooking and as a tea, which is a wholesome drink for the sick and the healthy and especially good for school-children.

The Latin name *Melissa* means Bee. It has also been given the name *apiastrum*, from *apis*, the bee. It was used as one of the sacred herbs in the temple of *Diana*; here the priestesses were signified as bees, and the High Priestess as their Queen.

Bee-keepers instinctively used to rub beehives with *Melissa* for the very reason that it would keep the swarm together and attract others. In fact, *Melissa* and the bees belong so much together that if the one had not become a plant and the other an insect, they might still be one being. The relationship of the Bee and Man is explained by spiritual science in the following way: "We find something in nature that is like a head, but a head without the enclosing skull, where the same forces are at work from outside as work within the head. A beehive is in reality a head which is open in every direction. The activity of the bees is the same carried on in the external world as that within the human head, only it is not enclosed, it is activated from outside. Within the beehive we find the honey and when adults eat honey it gives the same strength and power of those formative forces that the head receives in early childhood by drinking milk". From such relationships between plant, animal and man we can gain much understanding of nature.

The English name "*Balm*" is derived from the warming, comforting qualities of Balsam, whereas the common name

Lemon Balm is not only due to its taste, resembling that of lemon, but refers also to the high content of phosphorus, to its sanguine element of light.

There still exist some humorous sayings of country people, as, for instance, "*She has a bee in her bonnet*", or "*He is balmy*"—sayings which must have arisen from a former instinctive but degenerated conception of this herb.

In all this we should not overlook the fact that, at the slightest irritation, bees attack and sting. The nervous system responds in the same way to the attack of mental processes. What is needed, however, is a "*Doctor Universalis*" able to meet the sting that has been inflicted by the human intellect upon our present-day nutrition.

BASIL

Ocymum basilicum
Labiatae

In this country Sweet or Common Basil is not a popular herb—maybe the English climate restricts its cultivation. It is best sown early in March under glass, and after the late frosts have passed, the seedlings should be transplanted 6–9^{in}, (15.24–22.86^{cm}) apart. Outdoor sowings can, however, be made at the beginning of May in a warm and sheltered border of well-composted soil. As it is not a hardy plant, it must be treated as an annual.

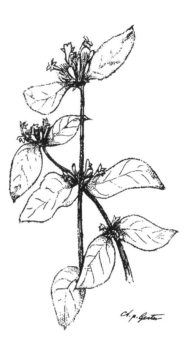

Basil grows up to a height of 2–3^{ft}, (0.61–0.91^{m}); the stems are quadrangular and carry opposite, hairy, greyish-green leaves. During July and August whorls of white flowers appear in the axils of the leaves. In a hot and dry summer the seeds will ripen, but in a wet season they mostly fail.

Herbalists describe the aroma of this herb in rather different ways. This may be due to varying geographical conditions-wet weather or lack of sunshine; certainly it reaches the climax of its incomparable flavour during a long hot summer. It has both medicinal and culinary properties and is used in *cooking meat, gravies, soups, pulses, stuffings and in salad dressings*. Also for making appetising *sandwich spreads*. Its strong aroma calls for use in moderate quantity.

The qualities of this herb are the subject of great controversy. In classical cooking it plays an outstanding part, but it has almost completely disappeared from the English kitchen. It is a strange fact that in the East it is revered as a sacred herb, whereas in other parts of the world it is in dis-

66

repute and is considered to be a herb of the devil. Yet, by an imaginative approach, we may find in its name the key to this mystery.

The word Basil seems to be related to Basilica, a name given to a building of traditional architectural style in Greece and Italy, which serves all social needs. It was used for commercial purposes, for the height courts where human rights were defended and crimes judged, and it was also devoted to the spiritual and religious life of the citizens. *Basilica* means "royal", "splendid", and *basilicum* signifies the robe of a king.

On the other hand, in mythology we hear of an animal known as a *Basilisk*, the king of the serpents, and to confirm his royalty he was endowed with a crown. According to Pliny it was an animal that did not impel its body like other serpents by a process of multiple flexion, but it advanced boldly and upright. It lived in the desert and there were several species: one burnt up anything that it approached; another was like a Medusa's head, its look caused instant horror and death. No other animal would ever go near it except the weasel, which advanced boldly to the attack, and when bitten retired for a moment to eat some Rue, a herb under the dominion of the *Sun in Leo*, which was the only plant that the *Basilisk* could not withstand. The weasel then returned to the charge with renewed strength and never retreated until its enemy was dead.

These two contrasting pictures bear a resemblance to the Being of man. The building, the *Basilica*, with its threefold social function, points to his royal palace or temple, i.e. his body. He, the crown of the Creation, is robed in his *basilicum*, his mantle, adorned with ermine, that spotless white fur of the weasel or stoat. Here man is pictured in his greatest dignity.

The *Basilisk*, the serpent, however, represents the lower animal-like nature—with all its passions and desires burning up everything within reach—whereas the King of the serpents with the *Medusa's* head is a picture of the nervous system which at every moment imperils the life-forces of the organism. We should be struck by death if the blood- stream did not constantly counteract its destructive nature.

Thus we can understand how such contrasting conceptions of one and the same herb may have come about, and that to the declining spiritual conception of nature the noble character of this plant appeared to be a herb of the devil. Yet within the higher Being of Man, which is the true King, lies the power to transform his own destructive animal-nature, and Sweet Basil acts in the same way within the food he eats. It is said that it penetrates the blood as quickly as poison does, and it will dispel all that is in opposition to life.

In the past, when the "*diaeta animalis*", a one-sided meat diet, was dominant, the virtues of the aromatic herbs were called in to counteract poisoning. Among these Sweet Basil was regarded as of sovereign order. This still holds good to-day, and we should reconsider its use in the kitchen to meet the attack of the thousand-headed Basilisk which has appeared in the field of nutrition.

This *royal Kruid*—as it is said in Dutch—should be given the best place in the garden.

MINT

Mentha viridis
Labiatae

Mint is one of the few herbs that are still much valued in cooking, and has a place in every kitchen garden. It grows up to 3^{ft}, (0.91^m), and throws out a number of square stalks with opposite leaves, which are strongly veined underneath and finely serrated at the edge. In August the small mauve flowers cluster around the stem and gather at its end in the form of an ear. The root system creeps and spreads quickly under the earth. It will grow in almost any kind of soil, provided that it has a good dressing of compost and plenty of moisture available; it also needs a sunny position to

improve its aromatic oil content, which is apt to deteriorate in a shady place. It does not produce seeds easily, and propagation is mostly done by division of roots. A bed of Mint lasts for about three years and should then be renewed. In order to overcome the frequently appearing rust disease, it is advisable to cut the leaves early, before the flowers develop, and several times more before frosts set in. It is a herb of strong vitality and the more it is cut the better will be its health.

Among the many varieties, the common garden Mint, or Spearmint—*Mentha viridis*, the very aromatic, round-leafed variety—*Mentha rotundifolis*, and the dwarf variety, Pennyroyal—*Mentha Pulegium*, are those most used for culinary purposes. They are used with **green peas, new potatoes, pulses, and also for salads, mint sauce, stuffings** and **egg dishes. Mint fritters** are much appreciated as a dish in early spring. A sprig of Mint is dipped into a batter and then fried in deep oil. These fritters can be served either as an addition to the main dish, or as a sweet, sprinkled with sugar and lemon.

Mint is, of course, also of great importance in **special diets**, for patients on a milk diet, or for sick babies; it prevents the milk from curdling, and is a good substitute for tea for children and patients or anybody who prefers herbal teas to stimulants.

Our aromatic Mints include Citrus Mint, Eau de Cologne, Pineapple, Apple Mint and others, and these are mainly used for refreshing drinks. The old custom of making Mint Jelly for the Christmas table has not yet been lost. Also the little cushions of dried herbs are still appreciated for the fine natural quality of their scent.

Among the medicinal varieties, Red Peppermint, *Mentha piperita*, predominates. We recognise it by its dark red-green leaves and stems and its deep red-violet flowers and, above all, by its strong fiery aroma. Its ethereal oil is widely used for all sorts of purposes and is in great demand.

On account of its outstanding properties, dried Peppermint should have a place in the medicine cupboard to be prepared for the ever-recurring colds. Unfortunately for many people, the English climate proves to be a good soil for rheumatic conditions. At the same time Nature is kind and provides us with preventives and remedies, all of which have their own particular virtues.

The English name Mint is derived from the word "mind", while the German version *Minze* signifies "gold coin" which corresponds to the English variety Pennyroyal, *Mentha pulegium*, that is, "royal mint". Some names are connected with the human organism, such as Lung Mint that rules the breathing, and Peppermint the digestive processes. Others are Heart Mint, Corn Mint, Ladies Mint, Mary's Herb, Star of Bethlehem, Cross Mint, Holy Black Mint, the latter obviously having been changed with the rise of Christianity.

However, all these different varieties conceal some therapeutical capacity by which they are able to deal with every indisposition of the organism. They relieve cramps as well as kidney troubles, comfort the heart, regulate the breathing, strengthen the memory, relieve depressions of heart and soul, and so on. We can indeed rely on their help in connection with more than forty maladies, and it is right to speak here of a manifold "Health Service', a comprehensive Service of Nature which makes us aware of how much the Mint family is capable of contributing to the welfare of Man. Fundamentally this is due to the therapeutic power of the Sun.

The Mint family came from the Far East, eventually settled in the Mediterranean countries, and from there spread over the greater part of the Earth. In classical times these herbs belonged to the Temple services and all other festive ceremonies. They also played an important role in the treatment of the sick, as well as in the specially developed hygiene of the human body. Each part of the body needed the corresponding herb for its treatment. The Mint herb corresponds to the arms, because it was dedicated to the constellation of the Twins in the Zodiac, one kind of Mint being spear-shaped, the other with a shield formation. When in the course of the year the Sun stood in the zenith, then these plants on Earth received from the Twins the much-needed Light and Warmth-energies of the Sun in order to forge the weapons for the forthcoming battle in Autumn of the Sun-forces against the darkness and cold of Winter; and for its combat were needed not only strong arms but also tending, nursing hands.

What still reminds us of this are the shield and spear-shaped leaves of the Mint herb, their healing forces and their true name: *Royal Sun Gold.*

MARJORAM

Origanum marjorana
Labiatae

Marjoram is a perennial plant with a creeping root stock which after a year forms a strong clump. It sends forth masses of square woody stems to a height of 2^{ft}, (0.61^m), bearing egg-shaped leaves of a dark green colour. Its purplish-red flowers appear from June onward, continuing right into September; the whole plant is penetrated by a balsamic aroma.

This herb also loves to flourish in the sun and it does best in dry light chalky soil. Propagation is mostly done by division of roots, but the best plants are obtained from seed. Germination is rather slow and may take up to three weeks. The seeds are so fine that 12,000 are counted to one gram; germination capacity lasts for 2–3 years. For drying, the leaves should be gathered before the flowering stage, and are best dried in the shade to avoid loss of colour.

There exists another perennial variety, Pot Marjoram, *Origanum onites*, bearing white flowers.

The annual variety, Summer Marjoram, *Marjorana hortensis*, is more widely used on the Continent. In Northern districts this variety does not survive frost. It has bright green leaves and, as an interesting distinction, the flowers appear in little green knots, which accounts for its common name of Knotted Marjoram.

To achieve good results it is best to sow seeds indoors in March, and transfer the young plants to the garden during May, after frosts have ceased. In warmer parts it may be sown in April; but late sowing mostly prevents the seeds from ripening. The aroma of this variety is sweeter and more delicate than that of the others; it improves still more when dried and is therefore more appreciated for flavouring.

These three varieties are mostly used as culinary herbs, whereas the wild Marjoram, *Origanum vulgare*, is used mainly in pharmacy. The specifically decorative variety with variegated leaves and pink flowers, *Origanum vulg. aureum*, together with the mauve and white flowering kinds, mingle harmoniously with the unobtrusive colours of the herb garden, and provide a treasure field for insects and bees.

Herbalists have regarded Marjoram as a herb of universal character which by virtue of its great warmth-forces puts right many complaints and discomforts, particularly digestive troubles. It relieves cramp, stimulates excretion, and has been found effective in the early stages of dropsy. There is scarcely a better herb for relieving a sour stomach or for loss of appetite. It frees the head from the effects of bad digestion or from cold, and the heart from depression, it strengthens the nerves, supports sleep and has a dissolving effect on swellings, boils, varicose veins, and so on.

Thus Marjoram contributes many essential qualities to our diet. It is used in cooking, either fresh or dried, in **meat, stews and stuffings, pulses or any foods rich in fat**. In spring and summer, the young leaves of Marjoram give an interesting taste to all kinds of **fresh salads and vegetables such as beans and new potatoes**, and being so excellent **a stimulant to appetite** it is indispensable in **special diet**, but excessive use spoils the taste.

Marjoram has come to us from the great herb garden of the East. It is found in abundance in the calcarious districts of Asia, North Africa and Europe. In Egypt it was dedicated to Osiris, the Sun-God, and in Greek and Roman times it was offered on the altars of the Temples, and had its due place in medicine.

The name *Origanum* has come from a very ancient source. "Oros" means the mountain and "*ganum*" bright, the Joy of the mountain. As related in mythology, Venus was the first to raise the herb Marjoram. She raised it from Mare, the waters of the great ocean, to the top of the highest mountain, and there it was to grow beneath the Sun, gathering the rays of his light.

From the name Marjoram seems to have been derived the name Margaret or Marjory, which means the Pearl. St. Margaret of Antioch, a most popular saint in medieval times, was one of the fourteen holy helpers who had overcome the dragon and died as a martyr in the third century. Many Christian churches were dedicated to her and also to St. George, who lived at the same time, and of whom crusaders reported that he gave them his help under the walls of Antioch. Later he became the Patron Saint of England. *St. Michael*, the leader of the Heavenly Hosts, was also the leader of the Christian warriors on Earth.

Yet there are also hosts of unrecognised servants and helpers in nature who are fighting under the leadership of the Sun for the life of man on the battlefield of nutrition. And one of them is *Origanum marjorana.*

HYSSOP

Hyssopus off.
Labiatae

This evergreen shrub with its solemn appearance adds a great deal to the undefinable atmosphere to a herb garden. Bearing all the characteristics of a Labiatae it grows up to 3^{ft}, (0.91^m), in height, forms strongly divided roots and numbers of square stems, which towards the flower become round, an indication of balance between the forces of the earth and the sun. The dark-green, narrow leaves stand opposite to each joint, and the flowers come forth in long spikes of intense blue from July onward. In August the seeds begin to drop and should then be collected. They retain their germinating power for 1-2 years. Although Hyssop is mainly propagated by division, the best plants are obtained from seed sown either directly after ripening or in spring. A light sandy soil is best. The highly aromatic leaves, stems and flowers are the source of an ethereal oil of a very fine and delicate odour, which is valued even more than oil of Lavender and is extensively used in cosmetics.

There are also pink and white flowering varieties and a dwarf one, *Hyssopus aristatus*, a very attractive compact rock plant with a flowering time up to November.

On account of its diverse healing qualities, Hyssop is greatly praised by the old herbalists and physicians. They had good reason to do so, as it was a cure for many illnesses, such as weakness of the stomach, muscular rheumatism, pulmonary troubles, bronchitis and asthma. Like camphor it has a warming and calming influence, it loosens tension and cramp, regulates excretion, stimulates appetite, enlivens the nerves, and altogether its healing forces seem to be effective in every part of the organism.

In nutrition, Hyssop plays a great part in counteracting the effects of meat, as well as those of leguminous vegetables. It should, therefore, be used in *soups, gravies, sauces, stuffings, stews, fish and game.* The young tender fresh leaves give a particularly interesting flavour to *salads and to pickled cucumbers, onions, mixed pickles, red cabbage, etc.*

Hyssop is one of the oriental herb treasures which are found in abundance in the West of Asia, in Turkey and around the Caspian Sea; from there it came via the trade routes to Europe. Its name is of Greek origin. Among the Arabs it is called *Azob*, in Hebrew *Ezobh*, which means "Holy Herb", an indication that it belongs to the chosen ones for the service in the Temples. We shall, however, understand this herb better if it can be seen in its relationship to Savory.

SAVORY

Satureia hortensis
Satureia montana
Labiatae

Savory is not of great significance as far as its appearance goes, but all the greater are its other virtues. There is a Summer and a Winter variety.

Summer Savory, *Satureia hortensis*, is a hardy annual with a strong root stock, from which grow forth many erect, hairy stems with narrow, tender leaves at each joint, and its white flowers with a hint of pink come out in June and July. The calyx contains four tiny dark brown seeds which ripen during August-September and remain fertile for up to two years. Seeds are best sown in spring in light, but well-composted soil, in a

sunny position. The leaves may be dried for the winter and are best picked before the flowers develop.

Winter Savory, *Satureia montana*, has gained preference because it is hardier and survives the winter. The woody stems branch out, and in the lower region carry small, dark green leaves of a spatulate shape, while in the upper part they become linear. Propagation is done by division. It does well in poor stony soil and needs to be in the sun.

In former times the medicinal properties of Savory were applied to the functions of digestion and respiratory processes, to revive the nerves and senses and to overcome giddiness and mental exhaustion.

The culinary qualities of Savory are complementary to Hyssop. On the Continent it is regarded as indispensable in cooking beans, and for this reason it is commonly known in Germany as *Bohnen-Kraut*, and in Dutch as *Boonen Kruid*, both names meaning Bean Herb. Because of its hot flavour it took the place of pepper long before Oriental spices had become popular. This is why in German it is also still called *Pfeffer-Kraut*—Pepper Herb. It is valued particularly in *special diets* where pepper and other hot spices have to be avoided. ***Its general use in cooking is similar to that of Hyssop.***

Satureia montana has come to Europe from the Mediterranean countries. Its name *Satureia* had been connected with the mythological beings *Satyrs*, but it also refers to *Saturn*. There is a myth which tells of an ancient Deity, Saturn, that after the dethronement of Jupiter he fled to Italy where he reigned during the Golden Age. Every year during the winter season there were celebrated in his memory the Saturnalia, which corresponded to the Christmas festival. During these festivities all public business was suspended, declarations of war and criminal trials were postponed, presents were distributed and the slaves were treated with great liberalities. The masters served at their feasts, at which Savory was used in a similar way as we use mint-sauce today. Thus, during the coldest time of the year, the all-embracing warmth of human hearts was offered up to Saturn, and in these celebrations Savory had its due place.

As a culinary herb, Savory has a special affinity to leguminous foods. This may best be understood if we consider the nature of legumes which, indeed, form a substantial part of our diet, particularly when they are used as a substitute for meat. They belong: to those plants which reveal more than others something of their pre-earthly conditions—as has been mentioned before in connection with other vegetables—when plants and animals were not yet separated into distinct beings. All living creatures were then embedded in a general albuminous atmosphere from which they imbibed their nourishment. Later some animals had preserved a more plant-like character and some plants more of an animal nature. Certain legumes expressed a great deal of the animal being in substance as well as in their outer appearance. Their protein comes nearest to animal protein, even nearer than milk. In contrast to the watery element of cucumbers or marrows, the sanguine nature of peas and beans is expressed in the "wings" of the flowers which, however, are tied to the stem; they cannot fly like insects or butterflies do, and the whole plant needs to be supported by a stalk—it needs a ladder to climb up into the air. In the German language this particular group is called, in a pictorial way, *Schmetterling-Bluetler*—Butterfly flowers. We have a wonderful picture in the story of Jack and the Beanstalk in which the cow was exchanged for some beans, and when these were planted they grew and grew and formed a ladder for Jack to climb up as far as the home of the great Giant. A good fairy advised him to take from the Giant the inheritance of his father, and having achieved this he cut down the beanstalk so that the Giant fell down dead. Ever after Jack and his mother lived on Earth in comfort and contentment.

By means of such simple pictures were people in the past taught something of chemistry, how, in this case Nitrogen was brought down from the atmosphere and fixed in the soil.

It is indeed an interesting fact that the family of the Leguminosae have not produced any culinary herbs but a great variety of nourishing foods. In the Classical Age the legumes were in disrepute, they were considered a food that fettered the soul too strongly to the body, like the butterfly flower is fixed to the stem and is unable to fly. The Pythagoreans, who had great astronomical knowledge, held the view that leguminous food endangered the human soul to become isolated from the stars, and they abstained from eating it. Without this link man would sink into a realm where he might become a distorted being like a Satyr, with a human head and with limbs and hoofs of an animal. Even among the butterflies there is one named "Satyr".

The name Savory indicates the savoury taste of this herb, whereas the Latin name *Satureia* expresses its uplifting forces of warmth. Being saturated with the element of warmth, it was considered to be a herb of Saturn. Hyssop, on the other hand, being of a complementary nature, was dedicated to Jupiter or Zeus, the Father of Light.

Such conceptions of former times of plants linked up with the ancient Deities obviously have changed under the influence of Christianity. Hence in its deeper sense the name Savory refers to the redeeming forces of the *Saviour.*

SAGE

salvia off.
Labiatae

The Salvias represent the largest group of the family of the Labiatae with about 500 varieties, of which the garden Sages are classified as *Salvia off.* and are used for both medicinal and culinary purposes. As all its relatives, Sage also flourishes best in the sun of the Mediterranean. There, masses of its intensely coloured flowers cover the dry, white limestone districts, and the air is heavy with its wholesome aroma.

This shrub grows up to 3^{ft}, (0.91^m), or more, carries a profusion of leaves which develop stage by stage in pairs, and are strongly marked by a network of veins. At the height of summer a wealth of purple-blue and red flowers open, each one like a minute lion's mouth that devours the fire of the sun to the effect that volatile oil permeates the whole plant with an aroma of a bitter but not unpleasant taste. The seeds ripen during September and keep their fertility for 2-3 years. Propagation is usually done by division of the roots. Although Sage prefers to grow on lime, it is adaptable to any kind of soil provided that it is dry, as in damp positions its flavour is apt to deteriorate.

From times immemorial Sage has been a herb of great renown. It had its given task in the Temples and its healing properties were highly esteemed by ancient physicians. In the great medical School of Salerno, Sage was regarded as the reconciler of man and nature, while an Arabian proverb said: "How can a man die who has Sage in his garden?" That this herb is endowed with exceptional gifts is expressed in the name *Salvia* from the Latin *salvare*, to heal, or to preserve.

The English name Sage refers to wisdom. In an old paper, *The English Doctor*, published in 1607, the following explanation had been given:

"In Latin takes the name of safety
In English Sage is rather wise than crafty,
Sith then the name betokens wise and saving
We count it nature's friend, and worth the having".

Bacon blamed physicians that they cared only for disease and not for the prolongation of life. Sage was valued for this very purpose. It has the capacity to retard the processes of declining faculties, to maintain the failing senses and the memory, to restore energy and to lift the depression of heart and mind. In the old herbal of Gerard, Sage is mentioned as a herb of the brain and memory. It prevents the limbs from trembling and preserves health. For such reasons the Chinese treasured Sage so highly that for some time the Dutch had a very profitable exchange for Tea. In Italy, France, Spain and other countries where oil is the main cooking fat, Sage plays an important part to assist digestion. On the whole it is used in cooking **meat**, for **stuffings, gravies pulses and especially soups.** We may learn to value this herb anew as a **drink** and as a **substitute for Tea**, particularly in cases where stimulants are not permitted.

In the flower and herb garden, the many varieties of Salvias are valued not only for their extraordinary display of colours but also for their attraction for bees; and wherever else we find Sage growing, we may behold with an inner eye its protecting, saving gesture, a gesture of blessing, which truly man can only give when he has attained the Wisdom of Old Age.

THYME

Thymus vulg.
Labiatae

The silvery grey Sage and the sombre dark green Thyme present us with a great contrast, and yet they complement each other in their character. Common garden Thyme is a well known perennial shrub with fibrous roots, numerous woody stalks bearing small leaves, and during the summer mon-ths is covered with tiny pinkish mauve flowers. Its very fine glossy brown seeds keep fertile for 2–3 years. The annual variety of Thyme should be sown indoors in March, or outdoors when late frosts have ceased. In cold districts it requires a sheltered position.

There are numbers of varieties, each with their individual flavour and different coloured foliage, and flowers, and the many creeping varieties are indispensable in making a picture of the rock garden.

Wild Thyme, *Thymus serpyllum*, is one of the outstanding members of the vegetation of the hills and mountains all over Europe, yet it has its real home under the Mediterranean sun. It is a modest plant with regard to its requirements of earth and water, but all the more does it imbibe the forces of light and warmth. For this reason it was much valued in medicine as a stimulant of warmth in the cure of colds, coughs, bronchitis, and to relieve cramp and colic and to assist digestion. It dispelled headache and giddiness arising from the metabolism and it was considered a strong defender of the nervous system and no less against rheumatism and blood poisoning. It also played its part in children's diseases such as whooping cough, rickets, loss of appetite, restless sleep and nightmares. From all such healing qualities 1 we may learn to appreciate its help also in nutrition, and being complementary to Sage it should be used in much the same way.

In its solemn appearance Thyme was regarded as a minute semblance of a Cypress, the Tree of the Dead. There is an old saying that no grave should be without the adornment of Thyme. This seems to be a faint echo of the old Egyptian culture where it played an essential part in the embalming ceremonies. In the Greek language, Thyme means fumigating; it was used instead of incense, and it held an important position in cosmetics. The scent of Thyme was assigned to nobility and bravery, and was given as a symbol of courage to those who had no fear of death. It is assumed that for these reasons the name of Thyme must have been derived from the Greek word *Thumus*, which means the moral courage that does not shun crossing the threshold to the other side of the world.

Sage renders its forces to the end of human life and endows old age with the Divine Wisdom of the Sun, whereas the fragrance of Thyme sets the serene mood for our loving thoughts of the departed.

There is a very old and close relationship between Thyme and the bees which, so it is said, goes back to the beginning of the world, and ever since the bees have inhabited the sweet meadows of Thyme. In the Classical Age the honey of Mount *Hymethus* had been treasured as a source of Divine Love. From that which the bees do in nature, by gathering the honey for the sustenance of man, we may learn that only on the "*hymethian fields*" of human love, spiritual nourishment can be found and gathered by those who dwell in the world beyond our earthly existence.

ROSEMARY

Rosemarinus off.
Labiatae

This evergreen shrub with its rough woody stems, its dark green needle-shaped leaves and their warm fragrance, has much in common with the Fir Tree which inspires the mood of Christmas. It may be for this and still other reasons that it is one of our most beloved herbs. At the end of April the pale blue, almost white flowers cluster round the stem, and as soon as they are over, the new leaves sprout forth, and they are ready for drying before the end of summer. Propagation is best done by division of roots or by cuttings taken in August. It likes well-drained, light soil, but is sensitive to cold; in a severe winter whole branches are apt to get touched by frost and die off.

Rosemary had a great function in medicine and cosmetics, for, as Culpeper says, "Its chymical oil, drawn from the leaves and flowers were of help in so many diseases that it must be spoken of as a plant of royal properties, because the Sun claims dominion over it". It was used to awaken the functions of the head, the memory and the senses, and to comfort the stomach and the liver. It was smoked as tobacco for coughs and consumption, and was a cure for all rheumatic complaints, and also helped dim eyes to procure clear sight if during flowering time the blossoms were taken every morning. A bath with an extract of Rosemary was used as an antidote to tiredness and lethargy of both body and mind. On the whole, it seems to have come into the world to assist the general well-being of man.

Its use in the kitchen has, however, almost ceased. At the time of the old English herb gardens, it was considered 5 a great fault of omission when meat was cooked without a little sprig of Rosemary. Today in the age of much contaminated food, its purifying qualities are required more than ever before. Therefore it should be applied not only to *meat stuffings, gravies and soups*, but it can be of general use in vegetarian diet as in *pulses, dumplings, rissoles, mixed vegetables, soups, egg and cheese dishes*.

This herb of royal standard is found in super abundance on the dry rocks of the Mediterranean where its aroma lingers in the hot mid-summer air. The French name *Incensier* refers to its place in religious ceremonies. Some herbalists derive its name from the Greek *Zhops*—shrub and *myrinas*—balsam. Others call it *Dew of the Sea*. One of the numerous legends gathered around this plant tells of Rosemary that it does not grow beyond the height of man, *i.e.* 5-6^{ft}, (1.52-1.83^m). During 33 years it increases in breadth, but will never grow taller than the Body of the Saviour. Another legend refers to the name Dew of the Sea:

"In the Golden Age of Mankind when human beings still dwelt in love and unity with the divine in heaven and on earth, there lived in the waves around the island of Sicily a beautiful maiden. She enjoyed the sunlight, loved the moving sea, the blue sky and all humans on the isle. They were happy people, for the gnomes, undines, sylphs and salamanders—all the elemental beings—worked and helped untiringly in the service of Man.

There also dwelt on that island, in the middle of a great mountain called Etna, a witch of great ugliness who was jealous of the contentment of the people, so she decided to enchant all the plants which so freely and in 6 such abundance served human beings. She took some of the evil herbs— Henbane, Mandrake, Nightshade—and stirred them in her cauldron, casting evil spells. Soon the plants, which until that time had been free and unfettered to the earth, were enchanted; they grew solid roots which would fix them firmly in the ground, their leaves contracted, became small and hard, and they could now see the sun only through their flowers.

Thereafter the inhabitants of the isle became very sad, even the sea grew angry and revolted against the evil witch. It was of no avail; all the witch had to do was to cast a spell over the sea also. Thus, gradually, the ocean too became enchanted. But there arose on the last wave a beautiful maiden, who promised to free all the land from this dreadful curse. The old witch chanted yet another spell, and the maiden was pulled down to the hard rocks of the sea shore. In making one last effort for freedom, she said to the plants all around: 'Remember, remember the Father who sent me to you; His Son will come one day to redeem us all'. With these words she changed into a lovely plant which clung to the rocks. In springtime she lifted her beautiful eyes to the Sun and she took to herself his light and warmth, so that all who would see her might remember her last words".

It is in fact this *up-lifting power of her eyes* that has become substance within this plant. Its sun forces have the strength through the blood to up-lift and to reinforce the Ego of Man, who on the rocks of the material world needs to keep upright and to be as erect as are the branches of Rosemarinus, and for that reason it held its old Latin name *Coronarium*.

LAVENDER

Lavendula spica
Labiatae

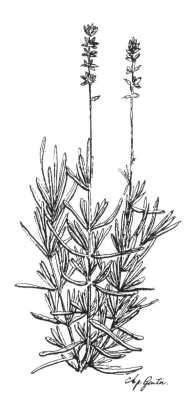

A remarkable contrast to Rosemary is its unpretentious but equal partner Lavender, of which there exist so many varieties that they alone could fill a herb garden. Its green or grey foliage grows in stages around the stem, and the tiny mauve to deep purple flowers are borne at the end of a long thin square stem after the fashion of an ear of wheat. In a normal summer the flowers are ready to be gathered from the middle of July, yet the climate of this country prevents its seeds from ripening and propagation is mostly done by division of roots or by cuttings taken in August. It does best in light limy soil and needs protection from cold wind and frost. The whole plant is permeated by a most delicate comforting scent. While Rosemary is a herb of a strong fiery character with the capacity of assisting the warmth processes and of strengthening the organic functions, its counterpart, Lavender, has a different disposition: it is of a calming, soothing nature which brings comfort to the nerves, relaxes tensions and relieves cramp; it quietens the blood stream and assists sleep. Like Rosemary it is mostly used in cosmetics for its aromatic and purifying properties, while in the kitchen it was famous for *flavouring sweets, drinks and for Tea*.

The name Lavender has been derived from the Latin "*lavare*", to wash, to purify the hands of the celebrant in rituals, "*manus meas in innocentia*". In German it means laben—in the sense of leben, to revive. Rosemary is related to Lavender, as the Spirit is to the Soul, or according to an 9 old proverb, as a Man to a Woman. The following legend illuminates this meaning:

"When God had created Adam and Eve and they dwelt in Paradise in happiness and bliss under the protection of the stars, two of the stars like two glorious eyes radiating Divine Love and Providence, watched over them day and night. As time went on and great dark shadows began to extinguish the light their two defenceless protégés were in danger of being torn away from their sight and guardianship. In the hour of their greatest need, each star decided to send a messenger with a token that would for ever remind them of their starlit home. The messengers arrived at the gate of Paradise just as the Cherubim lifted his flaming sword to expel Adam and Eve from the garden of Eden. While the Angel was closing the great portal, the two messengers tried to escape through the narrowing gap to follow them into a world as yet unknown. But the Angel held them back and said: 'No one must enter that land which lies yonder in utter darkness, the land which is destined to drink the tears of women and to eat of the never-ceasing longings of men'. The messengers were determined to carry out their promise, however, and the one said: 'I have been sent from the Kingdom of the Silver Fishes and my King offers this gift to strengthen man on his way'. And the other one replied and said: 'I have come from the Land of the Golden Harvest and my Queen offers this gift for his comfort'. When the Cherubim beheld these Divine tokens, he recognised his brothers and allowed them to pass through the gate, each one in disguise of a plant, to go with man on his way into the unknown. Ever since, they have followed him through all temptations, tribulations, sickness of soul and body, and have bestowed upon him strength and 0 comfort, endurance and resistance, life and health, and they will do so until the day when man of his own accord will again turn to his starry home, from whence he had come. Then Rosemarinus and Lavendula will have fulfilled their promise".

ONION

Allium cepa
Liliaceae

The Onion family represents a particular group of the Liliaceae which has produced plants of nutritious, culinary and medicinal value. The bulb of the onion bears all the chief characteristics of a flower-bud with the difference that it does not develop at the crown of the plant, but at its base. It enters just deep enough into the ground to keep in sight of the moon, as the old gardeners used to say. Instead of solid roots it pushes a bunch of white almost transparent root-tubelets into the soil and stores up to 90 per cent of water. The properties of this "bud" are similar to those of a flower, containing volatile oil of a very powerful pungent aroma, carbohydrates, latex, sulphurous and phosphorous elements and others. It does not open its petals, but its gesture is rather an enclosing one and causes the petals to turn into scales. Thus each of the six petals which mark the formation of the normal flower are here resembled by scales. These are protected by a papery skin, which according to variety may be brown or white, fused with green or purple towards the leaves. This kind of bud bears, of course, no seed but is able to reproduce itself vegetatively by throwing off new bulblets. The leaves, too, are closed up into a tubular shape and in spring come up from the earth like rays. In summer the real flowers develop in a peculiar way. The central leaf acts as stem and at its end forms a globe that carries masses of tiny white or mauve florets of hexagonal shape. The black seeds take their time to ripen and do not fully mature until they have had, according to an old saying, "the blessing of the full-moon at 3 Christmas time". Good seeds preserve their fertility for up to five years. The highest qualitative standard is reached in southern countries such as Egypt and Spain.

The Onion is a native of western Asia and is indeed one of the oldest of our cultivated vegetables. For thousands of years it has influenced the development of mankind by its particular function with regard to its generative and hereditary forces, as well as to its intellectual capacities. It played an important part in Egypt, India and China, in the tradition of the Hebrews and in Greek, Arabian and Roman culture.

The name Onion is derived from the Latin *unio-onis*, meaning a large pearl, and this in turn comes from *unosone*. Its meaning refers to the monotheistic principle of the Hebrew religion, as well as to the common characteristic of the monocotyledons. Amongst these we find the large group of the Liliaceae which have excelled in creating a splendid variety of beautifully coloured and scented flowers. They are some of the first to greet the spring and their extraordinary display culminates in the ideal manifestation of that family in the Lily.

It lies within the nature of a bulb to store up those forces and substances which are essential for the development of the new plant-embryo. Its watery element bears a formative quality that reveals itself in the strictly geometrical shape of its flower. We find even an outer indication of the regenerative forces of this plant in the peculiar type of the Tree-Onion, *Allium cepa viviparum* representing the picture of a family tree, a natural illustration of how one generation is linked to another. From all this we may understand that the 4 Lily was assigned to conception and birth. In Egypt the flower of innocence was dedicated to the Moon Goddess Isis with the Child Horus. In post-Christian times it appeared in many paintings of the Annunciation, of the Archangel Gabriel announcing the Birth of the Lord, the event when the monotheistic principle of Jehovah, the Moon-God was to be superseded by the Sun.

Among the members of the Onion family, the variety *Allium cepa* is mostly used in medicine. Its rich content of sulphur and essential oil assists the metabolism, and its great purifying quality is generally recognised. Today, it is still regarded as one of the universal home-remedies for frostbites, boils, bee stings, rheumatism, gout, coughs and as a preventive of the common cold.

Allium cepa and its relative the Leek, Allium porrum, are both used as **cooked vegetables**, while the Shallot, *Allium ascalonicum*, is preferred for seasoning. On the whole the Onion is more in demand for flavouring than any other herbs, therefore the ways of using it are best left to the artist in the kitchen.

For *babies* and *young children*, however, onions are <u>too strong</u>, and are unsuitable food for anyone with internal disorders. Fried onions are particularly indigestible and should be <u>omitted</u> from **<u>special diets</u>**.

In its minutest form, the Onion family is represented by the Chive, *Allium shoenoprasum*, which is a well-known member of the herb garden. It is easy to grow from seed or by division of clumps. The more it is cut, the better will it flourish and continue without loss of energy until late autumn. During its flowering Period, masses of mauve or purple flower heads make a pretty, colourful edging. This variety provides a milder and more delicate flavour that adds to the perfection of any **salad**. The Chive, representing the baby of the family, is more suitable to introduce the Onion into the diet of children. There is also a bigger and hardier brother of the Chive, the Welsh Onion, *Allium fistolosum*, which thrives and produces fresh green even throughout the Winter.

The Onion family is at its strongest in Garlic, *Allium sativum*. Since ancient times it had had its function in infectious diseases. It assists the circulation of the blood and the excretional processes, it strengthens the senses and raises the consciousness and mental faculties. In fact it was always looked upon as the great defender against all infirmities arising with advancing age, and as a plant that has been adapted by Nature for the prolongation of life. Thus, within this family, Garlic represents Old Age. Its outstanding flavour and smell restrict its use in cooking to a minimum—a touch, by rubbing the bowl with it, gives sufficient taste to a salad. Its presence in cooked food will be more acceptable if it is blended with other ingredients.

There is a saying that a clove of Garlic planted beneath a Rose bush upsets the Rose so much that in utter self-defence she increases her scent. Although the Rose hardly belongs to the subject of culinary herbs, yet taking into account the above saying and its sweet fragrance, it might be a still greater offence to the Queen of the monocotyledons, the Lily, if her counterpart, the Rose, the Queen of the dicotyledons, were left out of the picture.

ROSE AND LILY

Rosa canina (Rosaceae)
Lilium candidum (Lilioceae)

"Without the Rose and the Lily
My garden of 'Simples' is dark and chilly".

    In the days when a living conception of nature still pre-
vailed, human hearts expressed their feelings in such phrases
as the one above.

These words touch upon an inner characteristic of the two great figures in the vegetable kingdom which have been raised to the highest rank of all flower-bearing plants and thereby also to their due place in our culture.

Since times immemorial there existed an inexplicable power of attraction between Man and the Rose, which must have had its origin in a world other than our Earthly one. How else could this flower have partaken in the events of his life—in his joys and sorrows, in his wishes and their forgoing, his desires and their overcoming, in war and peace, and above all in his striving for his highest ideals? And how could it have inspired his Spirit to penetrate ever deeper into its Mystery? No wonder that since Man learned to read and write, more books have been written in the course of time in favour of this plant-being than about any other of its flowering companions.

Eastern traditions record that the original Rose had been awakened from its slumbers by the first ray of the rising Sun in the great Garden of Persia. Since then its seeds had been carried over all lands, though only as many ever bloomed as there were human Souls living on Earth. Yet 7 when a Soul knocked at the portal of the upper world and all material things had to be left behind, only her little red Rose was allowed to accompany her over the threshold.

In his *History of Plants*, Gerard, the great herbalist of the 16th century, recorded that the Turks did not like to see rose-petals withering on the ground because they had been told in their dreams that the Rose had sprung forth from the pure blood of Venus.

It is indeed so that something stirs one's conscience when masses of those lovely red petals are scattered over the ground, whilst their precious scent has vanished into the air.

A poet like Shakespeare$ knew well what to do about it by saying: "Of their sweet death are sweet odours made". A contemporary of his, a herb gatherer, gave the laconic advice: "Hold dried rose-petals to thyne nose, they comfort thyne brain, they quieten thyne heart and are quickening thyne Spirit".

In our century we have learned to save a maximum amount of time by having many technical tools at our disposal. Of such saved time-capital we might well use some during the summer and autumn for gathering rose-petals and converting them into health-capital by transforming them, for instance, into syrup. Rose extracts of this kind can strongly be recommended as an important asset to the diet of children as well as adults in place of some of the many modern means by which we try in vain to keep fit. We shall indeed find much comfort and benefit hidden in a small bottle of Rose Elixir, for instance, for the overstrained mind and tired nerves.

Furthermore, preserves made of rose hips, and tea made of the kernels, should by no means be regarded as a mere repetition of the past, and in days of growing need we ought to take notice of one of our most timely counteractions to the declining state of our present-day nutrition.

During the last decades the use of Roses has become an important field of scientific research with the aim of bridging the great gap between food and remedy, and making them available as dietetic preparations for general consumption.

Maybe that in the near future we shall gladly return to Nature for other helpful plants which may either have been forgotten or are still unknown to us, yet which Mother Earth may hold in store for greater needs to come. In fact there are all the indications that we shall have to learn once more to foster a simpler way of life, and by turning with more consciousness to Nature we may indeed hope for a better and healthier one.

In comparison with the Rose, the Lily has entered human culture in a very different way. Ancient records inform us that this plant-being arose from the purest waters of the Moon, and on descending to the Earth opened its first bloom in a most delicate form, revealing a sixfold star. Thus it became visible to Man, but not until after his Fall in Paradise.

Ever since, it has lived in his soul as an image of purity and innocence, of the unspoiled wisdom in early childhood that lights up once more in the heart of Man towards the end of his Earthly life. Thus has the Lily witnessed his coming and going, his birth and death—it is indeed the flower that has adorned his cradle as well as his grave.

In contrast to the iron strength of the Rose—being very much down to Earth by activating and encouraging the heart, the mind and the will of man—the Lily would appear to be standing aloof, hardly touching the Earth. Even so, it has fulfilled an immense task in the midst of all the practical necessities and work on the Earth.

On the basis of their relationship to the Moon and to the great family of the gramineous plants, the grasses, the Liliaceae have been qualified by Nature to provide Man with all the various types of cereals for his most staple food —his daily Bread.

The Rose, on account of its affinity to the Sun, has been given the complementary task to enliven Man by means of the many kinds of fruits of the Rosaceae, with the Elixir of the Sun—the Vine

This may shed some light on the old English custom when the Rose and Lily were revered as the Lord and Lady of all food and drink, for they reigned over the kingdom of the plant-world as Sun and Moon reigned over the starry universe. Then one still knew that food and drink did not sustain the human body alone, but at the same time they were the nourishment of Soul and Spirit. And this found its true expression in the simple words:

"The Lily and the Rose combine
The Wisdom and the Love Divine".

If with these words in mind and with open eyes, we go through Nature, we are greeted by countless images of this royal relationship of the Lily and the Rose. May it be in a field of corn surrounded by hedges of Briar Roses and Brambles; or in an orchard where many different types of 1 grasses surround the fruit-bearing trees; or on the way through woodlands where tiny bright red strawberries are peeping happily through the tender blades of grasses—such are the pictures that repeat themselves in ever-new variations and combinations. At last we may also enter into the more intimate milieu of the herb garden, where too the Lily and the Rose are radiating in the midst of the herbal flora. And it is here where two vital streams flow into one: the Glory of that dual Star and the healing virtues of the Simples.

THE FOOD WE EAT
A SERIES OF ESSAY ON NUTRITION AND COOKING

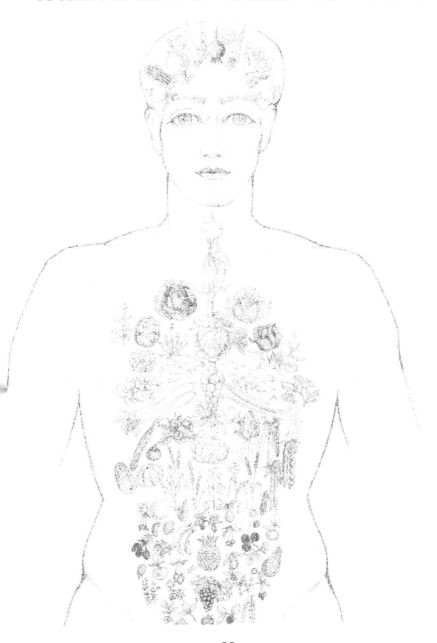

WHY SHOULD WE USE HERBS?[3]

SOME of the food products that we used to have are entirely missing today, or are only available in insufficient quantities. Certain substances therefore predominate in the human organism—one part of it becomes too strong and overrules the rest. The best example of this was given this past winter (1940/41) by the increased consumption of root vegetables and potatoes and the great loss of fresh fruit—by which our nutrition was thrown out of balance.

A diet which consists mainly of roots brings an excessive amount of salts into the organism whereby being only partially absorbed they form harmful deposits. Not only rheumatism, gout and sclerosis are the result of this, but also many disturbances arise from an over stimulation of the nerve-system.

With the restrictions in our choice of food today we feel like going back to the times when transport facilities did not exist which could bring fresh fruit, for example, from distant countries. How did people live in those days when vegetable cultivation in this country was hardly known and when potatoes had not yet appeared? Then meat was the ruling power in nutrition and with its strong mineral influence it accompanied the development of man on his way down to earth. To counteract the mineral processes it was necessary to apply healing forces in the form of all kinds of flowers and herbs.

For hundreds of years we only hear of herb-gardens, people at that time still knew instinctively, and out of old traditions that herbs were the bridge from nutrition to medicine. Many flowers and herbs were used in drinks—teas, wines, jams, salads, soups and stuffings.

If we consider the blossoms, we see that they take very little part in our food, yet they are just as essential as all other parts of the plant. Their effect on the human organism as well as on the soul-life lies in their power to dissolve cold and darkness with their warmth and light.

The scents and aromas of all the various herbs are flower qualities which the plant has sacrificed and taken into

---

[3]   First appeared in the Sunfield Letters 1941.

seeds, leaves, stems, bulbs and roots, and which there have become healing forces. When most of the herbs reach their flowering stage their best forces ascend into the honey which the bees like best. Here develops the sugar substance—the beginning of the fruit process of these plants. In the use of honey we receive not only the missing fruit sugar but also all kinds of hidden healing forces from the herbs.

Looking back again into olden times where the effect of one-sided meat diet had to be continuously healed, we could put forward the argument that the restricted use of meat today can do no harm. However the difference of this age from the middle ages lies in the descent of a great deal of our food into chemical conditions. For many people today hardly any food is left which has not been influenced by chemical processes or has gone through preservation by cold and darkness.

Thus we have become subject to still stronger hardening processes and diseases and therefore more than ever light and warmth have to enter our food by the dissolving and healing powers of herbs, flowers and honey as the necessary re-creation for our life-forces.

Therefore their use should be recognised as most essential in our present stage of nutrition.

HOW TO USE HERBS[4]

IF WE classify kitchen herbs according to whether they are roots, bulbs, stems, leaves, flowers or seeds, then their use can be explained more easily.

- ROOTS:—

    HORSERADISH—raw or cooked is good to eat with all kinds of cabbages and meat, and can also be used for pickling purposes.
    PARSLEY—for soups, boiled or roasted meat, fish or stews.
    CELERIAC—raw or cooked, for salads, soups, meat or vegetable stews.
    RAMPION—raw for salads.

- BULBS:—

    GARLIC—is not so commonly used because of its strong taste. French people only rub it round their salad bowls or use it with meat sausages, soups and legumes, for instance green lentils.
    ONIONS—are valued much more and are used in greater quantities than herbs, in all kinds of meat dishes, Stews, potatoes, cabbages, salads and gravy and yet their taste should not predominate.

- STEMS:—

    ANGELICA—for confectionery.

- LEAVES:—

    <u>ALECOST</u> - <u>BALM</u> - <u>BORAGE</u> - BURNET - <u>CELERY</u> - <u>CHERVIL</u> - <u>CHIVES</u> - CRESS - <u>COWSLIPS</u> - <u>DILL</u> - <u>FENNEL</u> - <u>HYSSOP</u> - MARIGOLD - <u>MINT</u> - MUSTARD - NASTURTIUM - TARRAGON - <u>SORREL</u> - <u>PURSLANE</u> - <u>RAMPION</u> - YOUNG VINE - WOOD-SORREL;—

All these herbs can be used fresh in salads, herb-sauces herb-butter and cheese-pastes. Those underlined may be used for all kinds of soups and vegetables.

Balm - Dill - Mint - Peppermint - Woodruff, soaked for ½ an hour in water in a covered vessel, are useful in summer for making refreshing drinks. When lemons and apples are not available the sour taste of sorrel is a good substitute.

Basil - Celery - Hyssop- Lovage- Marjoram - parsley - Rosemary - Rue - Sage - Savory - Thyme, are more used for

---

[4] First appeared in the Sunfield Letters 1941.

soups, legumes, all kinds of potato dishes, vegetables and meat stews, stuffings and gravy. Savory is a special herb for beans and broadbeans, and Tarragon, Borage, Fennel and Dill for Cucumbers. Dried Horehound - Hyssop - Peppermint - Rosemary - Sage - Thyme - Marjoram - wild Strawberry leaves are all useful for making hot drinks in winter.

- **BLOSSOMS:—**
    ACACIA - BORAGE - COWSLIP - ELDERFLOWER - DAISY - GILLYFLOWERS - HYSSOP - PRIMROSE - MARIGOLD - VIOLET - ROSE - ROSEMARY - TANSY - NASTURTIUM;—

All these flowers can be used fresh in salads, or dipped in batter and fried in deep oil, or in pancakes. They are also excellent preserved in sugar as candies or syrups. With their most delicate natural flavours and their healing forces they are a great help to sick people in winter, when there is no fruit. They may also be preserved in vinegar and used for salad dressings in winter. Those underlined are also valuable for teas.

- **SEEDS:—**
    ANIS - CARAWAY - CORIANDER - DILL - FENNEL - MUSTARD;—

Anis and Fennel are most essential for babies in teas, puddings, vegetables, and biscuits. Those underlined, having a great deal of warmth, are more essential for roots, potatoes, cabbages, meat, and cheese. These seeds will be of great value where other spices like pepper, curry, nutmeg, etc., are not procurable. I advise those who have a garden to plant sufficient of these herbs in spring (March) in order to be provided with spices in autumn.

Nature provides many kind helpers to protect us from disease, and to stimulate not only our digestion, respiration, circulation and nerve processes, but also our mind and soul.

THE USE OF HERBS IN COOKING[5]

THE USE of herbs in cooking should always make us aware of the fact that we build a bridge from nutrition to medicine. We should regard them as remedies that need to be used homoeopathically[6] rather than in large quantities. In the same way as we take medicines in a certain rhythm when we are ill—should we also use herbs regularly and conscientiously, according to the food which needs to be harmonised. Then no disease-creating powers are allowed to accumulate in the organism but are constantly dissolved and excreted. A disease enters the organism from the earthly realm either through excess of, or insufficient forming forces from the mineral world. Or from above by soul forces that either penetrate the organism too powerfully, or through under-nourishment and defects, are too weak to take fully hold of the body.

This makes us realise that we have to take into account not only the nutrition process in which food substances go through the digestive processes and are taken up by the blood. But also the nutrition in which insubstantial qualities feed the soul through the sense perceptions via the nerves.

For example, an over-stimulation by common salt causes too much consciousness of the earthly world. The nerve-system becomes irritated by too many sense perceptions and we rather like to see them going up in the smoke of a cigarette and disappearing into supersensible conditions. On the other hand if our senses of taste smell and sight have not sufficient perceptions of colour, aroma and taste in the food we eat, then from that part of the senses the soul does not get much nourishment and is in danger of becoming inactive, poor, dull and feeling less interested in the world.

We should become much more awake to the need for colours. The sight of colourful dishes and of flowers on our table, is indispensable in the perfection of a meal. ... Besides the colours we have to consider also the scent of flowers and

---

[5] First appeared in the Sunfield Letters 1941.
[6] Homoeopathically in this context is used as a simile, meaning in small quantities taken rhythmically and not made into a homoeopathic medicine.

herbs, which stimulate our sense of smell; and of the same importance are all the various tastes.

In a special study of tasting herbs we find a scale of seven tastes, which can be distinguished most easily in the following:—

Aniseed	-	sweet	-	seed and blossom
Coriander	-	oily	-	"
Mustard	-	hot	-	"
Parsley or Lovage	-	"herb"	-	leaf and stem
Sorrel	-	acid	-	"
Sage	-	bitter	-	root-like quality because of their hardness.
Rosemary or Savoy	-	salty (in a mineral sense)		

All these different qualities our sense of taste has to apply for its development, just as in our sense of hearing it has to apply the scale of seven tones in the realm of music, or our sense of sight a scale of seven colours in the sphere of painting. The use of these favouring qualities in preparing food therefore calls for the corresponding artistic capacities that are necessary in the use of tone and colour in art.

By the conscious perception of tastes we build the bridge from the root to the upper part of the plant, to blossom, fruit and seed—from the earthly quality of salt to the heavenly quality of sugar. In the combining of the two opposite worlds by our senses we find not only nourishment but also harmony for our soul.

THE USE OF OIL IN COOKING[7]

I have often been asked for an explanation about the use of oil in cooking. Our traditional cooking fats consist mostly of animal fats—lard, suet, dripping and butter.

As a result of experiments carried out at the end of the last century whereby certain fats were solidified into a butter substitute, a new fat became available for cooking, known as "margarine". The prejudice against this substitute, especially against whale-oil margarine, was easily overcome, when science was able to remove all doubts as to its hygienic properties.

Thus margarine became one of the most indispensable modern foodstuffs being far cheaper than butter, in flavour and appearance sometimes hardly to be distinguished from it. Even the chemical composition is similar to butter and the only missing quality, the vitamin, has also lately been introduced.

Whatever type of butter substitute, animal, vegetable, or mixed margarine, is produced, a certain amount of skimmed milk is necessary for its consistency and, as with butter, the regulations allow not more than 16% of water content.

Vegetable margarine is produced from basic. Oils which are hardened by hydrogenating processes, or from coconut or palm kernel oil—which is nearer to real butter—and also from liquid oils produced from cotton seeds, peanut (arachis), soya bean, nuts, sesame, or linseed.

In cooking with margarine we are using all these oils, but we can and should learn to use them in their natural liquid conditions without their having to undergo the solidifying process.

In southern countries as where the sun's heat does not allow the hardening of butter, *olive* oil is generaly used instead. Whoever has tried to cook with olive oil knows that the toughest fowl or the hardest winter vegetable reaches a tenderness that no other fat can be achieved. Olive oil has the finest quality of all edible oils and therefore is also the most expensive. Most other cooking oils are usually cheaper

---

[7] First appeared in the Sunfield Letters 1941.

than margarine and more economical in use because of their greater fat content.

A number of oil seeds could be produced in this country. For instance *Walnut* is known as one of the best oils. *Filbert* (Hazelnut) oil is a good substitute for olive oil *Beechnut* oil which is chiefly used on the continent has the advantage of not easily turning rancid. During the first war the beech forests of Germany were one of the main sources of fat and schoolchildren during their autumn holidays were occupied in collecting the nuts.

Hempseed also yields an edible oil and *Linseed,* oil and *Rape,* oil are used all over Europe for human consumption. *Poppy-seed* oil is one of the best oils and is also used a great deal on the continent. There are two varieties: the white-seeded one, which is mostly used for opium, and the dark bluish-grey one which is used for oil production. These seeds are also used as an addition to bread or as flavouring for rolls and confectionery.

Sunflower-seeds could provide a great contribution to the fat production in this country. ... From an ounce of seeds the flowers will normally yield about 1 cwt of new seeds, each flower producing about 2,000. The oil content is about 40%.

The commercial extraction of oil from home-grown seeds would be something well worth while developing.

Sunflowers are a great help where bees are concerned and the seeds can also be a useful addition to poultry food.

*   *   *

In cooking with oils we should widen our ideas and should realise that all the different oils and fats have their own particular tasks in human nutrition, just as much as the minerals, starches, sugars and proteins have.

The use of the various plant oils in cooking can be explained in the following way. If in one menu we chose potatoes and swedes both cooked in peanut oil we would be making a very unbalanced meal, since both these vegetables and the oil all grow under the surface of the earth. What we ought to do is to balance the lower part of the plant by cooking it in oil such as Hazelnut oil which comes from the upper part of the plant. In contrast to the nerve-stimulating salt process of the root, it has a nerve-calming effect. On the other hand if we are making apple or elderflower fritters, it would be right to balance the fruit and flower process by frying them in *peanut* (earth-nut) oil.

These examples may show how we must develop a much greater consciousness of the combination of foods that we eat, and we must learn to use all the various oils as necessary complements to the various processes of the plants which constitute our vegetables.

Frying in deep oil is one of the most economical ways of using fat if we keep the oil in a special frying pan and do not transfer it to another container after use. What is most essential is to clean the oil after it has been used and while still hot by frying a dry crust, rusk or toast, or even some onion, in it until it has become dark. This will then have absorbed any foreign taste from the oil.

A little experience in this direction will soon overcome any prejudice we may have against using oil in cooking vegetables.

If instead of just boiling cabbage in water, as we usually do—we heat some oil, with a few slices of onion and tomato, add salt, pepper, mace, mustard seed, caraway seed, a little water to prevent frying, then stew the cabbage for 1 ½-2 hours—we will find that it is entirely penetrated by the oil and has become light and tender, easily digested and its taste will have greatly improved. If we tried the same experiment with lard we would soon see which was better.

Nearly all vegetables can be prepared in a similar way with different herbs and spices but the finer vegetables like spinach or green peas require less cooking. The prolonged cooking or stewing is essential for vegetables of a more material nature such as roots and all the various kinds of cabbages and dried leguminous (pulses) foods. In being slowly penetrated by the sun-forces of the oil the food undergoes a kind of warmth process that can be compared with the ripening process of seeds through the sun's heat.

Nature takes time in its cooking (ripening) process in Summer, whereas our modern requirements ask only for speed in cooking. However practical experience shows that a vegetable carefully prepared throughout, and slowly stewed with the suitable ingredients becomes a new creation—a new

plant organism whose various parts are represented as follows:

root	-	salt
bulb	-	onion
leaf	-	cabbage
flower	-	mace
fruit	-	tomato
seed	-	pepper, mustard, caraway, etc., and oil

In this way we can replace the mechanical ideas which pervade our cooking by living creative processes in which all the parts of the plant organism are represented in one dish.

The present limitations to our staple foods may even force us to take a wider view of the way in which the world of plants can serve our needs.

THE FOOD WE EAT[8]

The nourishment of the human being presents us with one of the most urgent questions of the day. Not only the bodily existence, but also the whole inner life of Man, is influenced by the food he eats. Under-nourishment or over-nourishment can be damaging to the Soul just as well as to the Body.

Human thinking will become increasingly one-sided and materialistic as long as Man is forced to be dependent on food-products that his cleverness has severed from the living forces or Nature. To free him from this one-sidedness, it will be necessary not only to consider the substances and forms of Nature, but to penetrate to those forces that have created these substances and forms.

Man is not able to create a plant, but he can direct his consciousness towards those hosts of forces which by their united work create our plant world in its countless forms—in all its beauty, and in its manifold use. This can awake in us the deepest admiration and wonder, and this admiration and wonder are the first steps on the path that leads to a real understanding of the creative forces that build up our Body and Soul.

Much valuable work has been done in investigating the material substances of food. Our task for future progress will be to include in our research those unseen forces that transform dead inert matter into living growing organisms.

In the study of Nutrition there are today two ways open to us. We can allow our conception of the nourishment of a human body to sink down to the level of a chemical industry. Far better we can uplift it to the altar of Life where it has its true place.

*   *   *

He who with inner courage breaks through the walls of our modern science of nutrition will find himself in a sphere in which everything is Life. Then he will have to realise that it was only his one-sided thinking that had held him back from penetrating into this world.

---

[8]   First appeared in the Sunfield Letters 1939.

A real sense for the Wonder of Nature can lead to an interest so warm and true that through it one can experience that the up-building forces of the human organism are processes of Life working in interplay between Nature and Man.

Within the realm of these Life-processes, the four great Powers of Nature meet one another, the Powers of Earth, the Powers of Water, the Powers of Air and the Powers of Warmth. Each one imparts the stamp of its own bodily form, and in their mutual interpenetration they weave together the Human Being in his material body, his blood circulation, his breathing and his warmth processes. No one of these forces can live without the other, and as they work together in Nature, so do they work in the Human Being—in harmony or disharmony.

It must be our task to recognise these forces as the creators of our life, and in deepest thankfulness to learn to receive what they have to convey to us.

One of the special characteristics of these Elements is that, for the life-purposes of Nature and of Man they go into imprisonment. They are continually looking to Man—as the bearer of human consciousness, and for whom they sacrifice themselves in his service—to set them free by directing his consciousness towards them. For they are always striving to unite again to return to their true home.

This imprisonment takes place most strongly in the human head and in the Earth. Tremendous strength is necessary to unlock this prison for those thoughts which are **not** in accordance with the idea of the Conservation of Matter. The worst kind of imprisonment caused by just such ideas as that of the Conservation of Matter, and this will always revenge itself in the most terrible way—for no human being can stand against the forces of the Elements. An example of this is seen in such a frightful catastrophe as the recent earthquake in Chile (1939).

As many hardening ideas as are in the world—so many releasing forces are also at work.

In a modern teaching of Nutrition, it is necessary that the four Element-bodies described, should be understood and cared for in the right way.

We take our nourishment from the Kingdom of Nature through Animal Plant and Mineral. How the Animal substances work into the human organism will be characterised next.

*   *   *

In the following discussion about food-stuffs taken from the animal kingdom, it must be made quite clear that the question is not one of propaganda—or for any particular kind of diet—but purely one of gaining insight into the effects.

The substances from the animal kingdom that we make use of for our nutrition are: Milk, Honey, Eggs, Fish and Meat, Milk and honey are taken from the living processes of Nature in which the light and warmth of the sun are at work. They have an exceptional task to perform in the nourishing of man.

Through the milk the small child is enabled to build up his body. Since milk contains all the substances which are necessary for this process. For a certain time it is the only nourishment for the child before he is capable of dealing with other food in his organism. Milk and the products obtained from it—butter and cheese—are the foods that connect man in a healthy way with the earth and make him an inhabitant of it. Milk has its place at the entrance to human life—at birth.

When during his development man becomes less dependent upon milk, especially with increasing age, then the honey takes on a special task within the organism. We know that the bee has forces out of which it can form the honeycomb in a very clever way. These forces are also in the honey, and when the human being begins to grow weaker in his limbs, then honey is able to replace the firmness that is lacking. Thus the honey stands more towards the end of our life.

Many wonderful things can be said about the two food substances mentioned above, and a whole lifetime would be necessary to discover all the secrets of the "Land flowing with milk and honey."

When we take animal-flesh into our organism we are exposed to forces of quite a different nature. Meat is not taken from life, but from death and darkness. The milk foods help

112

us to enter into a healthy contact with the earth. The use of meat however, fetters man to the earth, and he becomes earthbound.

Man and Animal can take directly from Nature, the plants which cosmic forces have conjured up, and through their digestion can transform them for their own nourishment. In this they are continuing a process that has already been carried to a certain point by the plant.

The animal has thus transformed the plant and made us of it for its own life-processes. If man eats animal-flesh, his organism does not need to do the work that it ought to do, since the animal has already done it for him. Many forces would have been called upon which now remain unused and are condemned to inactivity.

In fish diet still less demand is made upon the activity of the organism because fish live chiefly upon dead organisms.

One could imagine how within our organism many activities stretch out for work and yet are doomed to unemployment; in these ways functions are weakened or killed, and all kinds of deposits and hardening processes in the body resulting in illness.

Thus we see how a meat diet causes a certain weakness in the organism. Where it has its strengthening effect however is the region of the soul, by way of the blood. That the soul works upon the blood, we can see when a human being blushes with joy or grows pale with fear. Since man takes into himself not only the meat but with it the blood of the animal as well, an effect on the human blood and therefore on the human soul is inevitable. The soul-life of an animal can be much stronger than that of a man, in fact it can even overpower him completely, otherwise man would not flee from a wild bull. On the other hand there are human beings whose soul-powers are so strong that they can tame animals.

Here it must be specially pointed out that a child is not ready to grapple with these animal soul-forces before it has developed its own soul-life.

It remains for each one to judge for himself, whether animal or human soul-forces are to direct his life. We may well ask ourselves whether man cannot unfold sufficient energy to make his soul so strong that the support of the animal soul-powers simply becomes superfluous.

*   *   *

In the realm of human nourishment, eggs are in a certain sense the opposite of meat food. Meat is taken from the fully formed organism of the animal, not in a living but in a dead condition. The meat works in a strengthening way upon the soul-life, but in a weakening way upon the bodily organism—*it binds the human being to the earth.*

The egg on the other hand, is still on its way towards becoming a living organism—it is really still in a pre embryonic condition, and the soul of the animal has not yet taken possession of it. There are consequently no animal soul-forces present in the egg, which through the process of nourishment could stimulate the human soul as in the case of meat.

Thus through the egg food the soul is not called upon, is not stimulated, but sinks into comfortableness and inactivity—it becomes drawn away from the earth as if in sleep. Indeed the cause of such soul-conditions as listlessness and laziness can often be traced to an excess of eggs in the diet.

Albumen is nevertheless the basis of everything organic, and the egg food can also have its *strengthening* effect in the organism. There is however, a difference between the plant albumen that is the result of a hereditary process.

It must be mentioned again here, that the small child is not yet capable of dealing with these latter forces in its organism. In fact for a baby it can be a direct hindrance on its way from heaven to earth, if it is burdened too soon with an egg diet.

Thus animal albumen *strengthens the organism* but *weakens the soul*, and it leads to the human being *away from the earth.*

This tendency of the soul to want to leave the earth, was experienced in olden times then Spring came and the Nature powers resurrected from winter's grave into new life. The festival of the Spring-Goddess Ostera, or Eastera, was then celebrated (our present Easter Festival). Offerings of eggs were brought as a token of the Life which does not allow man to perish into mere earthliness, but ever again tears him away from the hardening forces until at death he leaves his body and returns to the sphere of Eternal Life. A feeble echo of this is seen in our present-day custom of giving Easter-eggs.

In the course of time human consciousness has had to deal more and more closely with the earthly element, and to guard itself against being led away from the earth. It was a healthy instinct that led Man to try to stimulate the soul and keep it down upon the earth by nourishing the senses with colour. Just as in Spring the flower-carpet of Nature makes the surface of the earth so beautiful that Man is loath to leave it.

In this way arose the idea of painting the Easter-eggs in bright and varied colours, also in many districts the old tradition of eating the Easter lamb is still observed.

The animal substances are thus used in the Easter customs as a token that the human being is placed within the everlasting struggle between Life and Death.

Two powers accompany the human soul in its sojourn upon the earth. The one, which continually seeks to fetter the soul to the earth, and the other, which would always like to tempt it away from the earth. The true worth of Man lies in holding the balance between these two powers.

One of the spheres of action of these two forces, is the whole process of nutrition:

> The meat diet that binds to the Earth.
> The egg diet that estranges from the Earth.

Milk and honey however, are the two animal food-substances which hold the human being in balance between Heaven and Earth.

We must win our way through the powers of temptation, to the "Land flowing with milk and Honey". Here we find ourselves in the Garden, which is enchanted into the human "life-body" and which must arise again from the grave of our present-day science of nutrition.

Whoever awakes in this Garden, will also find the Gardener, and will experience that it is He who holds out to him

> The Dish with the Bread
> His Body
> For All.
>   *   *   *

Plant-food diet is much discussed today—it is clung to by some in a fanatical way, and dismissed by others as inadequate.

The recognition of its value cannot lie in strict acceptance or refusal, but its necessity can only become apparent out of an insight into the continuous and progressive development of the human being.

In any case we must take into account that this development is always subject to hindering forces which also make themselves felt in the sphere of nutrition, but which we can recognise if we have sufficient power of discrimination.

In its extreme form—raw diet, plant-food makes the greatest demands upon the human organism, which must gather up all its forces if it is to do the work that would otherwise be done for it in the process of cooking.

This straining of the forces strengthens and hardens the bodily organism, and increases its capabilities just as hard work strengthens the muscles. But since the digesting of cooked foods, forces have to be borrowed from that part of our organisation that belongs to our inner soul-life, this becomes weakened and undernourished, and no longer equal to the demands of the present day.

For this reason so many people turn back in their inner life to spiritual streams of the past, since it is easier to bold to traditional ideas that demand no new powers of development and no new impulses.

For such people it is nevertheless still a satisfaction to be able to see the question of nutrition in connection with the spiritual life.

In our present day science of nutrition it is quite different. Spirituality and Nutrition have become separated, they go their own ways because the Soul of Nutrition—the Art, which should bind both together, is no longer there. Nutrition has been taken out of the Hands of Art, and has become imprisoned within the Head of Science.

The Art of Nutrition stands there like a beautiful old Madonna-picture whose colours are faded and whose content is no longer recognisable. A scientific painter covers it with synthetic colours in order to restore it, but it is no longer the same picture. Our Nutrition is thus glossed over with synthetics—and this is good enough for a cut-and-dried scheme of humanity that is no longer concerned with Individuality.

If the human being has not the will to discriminate, he will be entirely cut off from the true life-giving forces, his organism will harden, and he will be completely overcome by earthly powers. On the other hand his intellect can be carried to such a point that it must use its very creations as weapons against its own self thus the outer shell of this whole question must be cast off before we can find the real kernel.

*   *   *

In order to arrive at a deeper understanding of plant foods it is necessary to consider the plant according to its real nature, which reveals itself as a threefold being in:

•   Roots, Stems and Leaves, Blossoms and Fruits.

This threefold plant-organism is closely related to the threefold human organism in that within the process of nutrition the roots stimulate the head-powers, the stems and leaves the breathing and circulation processes, and the blossoms and fruits the forces of the metabolism.

It is however, in a one-sided way that the plant collects the nutritive forces for the human being—either in the roots, in the leaves or in the fruit. In the case of the carrot plant only the root is edible, with spinach it is only the leaves, with rhubarb the stem, and with the apple tree only the fruit.

There is no plant that can in this way nourish all three systems at the same time. Thus roots, leaves or fruit can only represent parts of the entire human organism.

The harmony of this combination however, cannot consist in a mere equal distribution of substances and forces within the organism, (and just in this every abstract scheme of nutrition breaks down) but in an individual consideration of the necessities of life.

In this sphere even the mere consideration of the individual temperaments can teach the greatest secrets.

In exactly the same way that the plant develops one-sided root-forces so the human being can develop his head-powers in a one-sided way when roots predominate in his diet. His metabolic system can be brought into disorder

117

when he eats too much or too little fruit, and weak lungs can be the result of too little leaf vegetables.

Moreover the extent to which the food should be cooked is also dependent on an insight into the individual needs. Whatever the human being takes from the threefold plant organism in his individual nourishment, there is one force that permeates the *whole* plant organism—the Sun-force.

This Sun-force in the plant food creates Light in the human organism in contrast to those foodstuffs that spread Darkness around them. Our whole problem of Nutrition is deeply involved in the battle between Light and Darkness which is taking place in our whole social life.

The forces of the Sun's light and warmth are taken up into the human organism through the plant food. The working of these forces is at its strongest in the blossoms and fruits. The fruits, which have to undergo the process of ripening, collect so much of the Sun's 'fire', that they are the best able to strengthen the process of digestion.

In the stems and leaves, the sun-forces begin to encounter the forces of the earth. Here Light and Darkness hold one another in balance. Where however, the dark earth-forces predominate, as for example in the cabbage variety and still more in the root vegetables, here Nature herself has given us the best balance in the herbs and spices.

The task of herbs and spices is to bring Light and Warmth into the earthly substances that provide our foodstuffs.

In some cases this "balancing" is done by the plants themselves, where the warmth and sweetness of the blossoms are sacrificed to the roots. This may be seen in the horseradish, and in the carrot and beetroot where even the *form* of the blossom may be seen by cutting through the root.

This balancing by means of herbs and spices comes into consideration for all the more earthly foodstuffs. Most strongly for the potato which unlike the roots of other plants that strive upwards towards the light, in reality is a stem which tries to struggle back into the earth. It tries to escape from the light, and is the one food which more than all other plants bring the forces of Darkness onto the human head.

The use of the potato as a staple food has accompanied our whole materialistic age and is very much connected with the materialistic tendencies in our thinking. This we can begin to overcome with such a herb as caraway seed for example, which brings an element of light and warmth into the food. In this way the herbs and spices do not work directly as articles of diet, but bring healing forces into the nutritive process—they build the bridge from the Art of Nutrition, to the Art of Healing. If they were to be used again in the diet with more consciousness and understanding, then many illnesses could be avoided.

The Darkness that enters our organism through the plant, is a natural and necessary one. Unnatural Darkness, which is not able to enter the living battle with the Light, and which is cut off from the forces of Life, is however, taken up into our organism through the modern artificially preserved foods.

In old Egypt the corpses of the human beings were mummified. Today the same thoughts of preservation and conservation are applied to foodstuffs, so that we actually begin to mummify not the dead, but the living being.

We live at a time where in our Darkness we must reach out towards the Light, so that we may learn to discriminate and to recognise who it is that offers us our bread:

The Tempter—or the Christ?

THE PLANT A MEDITATION[9] (1)

IF WE ARE to bring the laws of life of the plant world into our civilisation—it is important that we first learn to know the being of the plant itself. Upon this knowledge, as on a firm foundation, we are able to build with surety.

In this case it is a great help to experience the growing process or the plant. We take a seed and lay it in the earth with the consciousness that there is already pictured within it the spiritual image or the new plant, and that the earth and the heaven together have the power to bring this image into earthly form.

After a short time the outer covering of the seed breaks, and the seedling pushes through the enclosing surface of the earth. The first little leaves spread forth their arms in release at becoming free from the darkness.

It is important to experience within oneself the striving of the plant; for it strives for nothing less than the highest— for the heavens.

On the other hand the root develops, and through it the plant is held fast and bound to the earth. The root strives with the same power inwards to the earth as the other part of the plant strives outwards to the sun. We see in the plant two opposite directions of growth. The one strives upward, the other downward.

It is important to realise also how a boundary is set to the growth of the plant into the earth, also the other part of the plant, when it has developed stem and leaves, comes to its limit above. When it has reached this limit, the plant unfolds a new stage of development. The powers which until now have been used for the growth of the plant can no longer work in this way, and gather themselves together in forming the bud. Now the plant reaches the highest point of its development, when, on the waves of the light, the plant's soul, in colour and scent, is borne into the blossom.

If we open by force a closely shut bud, we find that it is still quite green and that at first only the outer petals slowly take on colour. As the bud opens so the colour is drawn

---

[9]   First appeared in the Sunfield Letters 1940.

more deeply into the flower until it slowly withdraws from the earth on the wings of the scent. Then the plant dies and that which remains behind is the seed that will give birth to the new plant.

The whole life of the plant fulfils itself without consciousness of its own process of development. It follows willingly but without desire an invisible power and conforms to the laws of its being. Its life takes place in sleep so that nothing from without can disturb these laws.

As a contrast, the living human being, besides the period of time that he spends in sleep, has also a great part of his life in a waking state. However even in our waking consciousness, we are still asleep for many things in life. As far as our observation goes we consciously take in the outer world, but, on the other hand, we are asleep with regard to the inner world. There is no outer world without an inner world.

In the inner world we need to awaken in the same way as in the outer would—and to learn to observe in it so that we can all the more understand the reality of the outer world. For example, we are asleep today with regard to the inner world of speech. The word "plant" describes something that is implanted into the earth as the outer form of the plant. We also find ourselves asleep to the inner world of the "plants". Only when we awake to it, does it reveal to us that it bears within it the word "plan". It shows to us that the plant contains the plans for all organic life on earth and is in its reality, the carrier of the life-plans of God.

What the plant is without will, man should be with will-awaking for his highest task. Which is; out of his own free will, to carry out the plans of God on earth, with a newly arising civilisation, and to raise the social life of mankind to a level corresponding to the plant of a higher order.

THE PLANT A MEDITATION[10] (2)

IF WE PLACE a seed into the earth we know that the spiritual image of the plant is already present in the seed and comes after a certain time into outward appearance. A healthy development from the seed into the plant can only be expected if the soil in which it grows provides the necessary conditions.

If humanity reaches a new stage in its evolution, its primary image is also present in the spiritual world like the image of the plant in the seed. It appears to us in its earthly form like a strange plant that fades away again and leaves its seeds in those souls who have been awake enough to be witnesses of the beginning of the new epoch.

In order that these seeds can unfold, a corresponding soil of thoughts has to be prepared.

The fundamental thoughts of each new epoch are also the same thoughts which think out the means by which the earth can be cultivated for the plants to provide food.

If from this point of view we look on to our agriculture, we find that it is an absolute revelation of the thought-content of the materialistic world-conception. The present conditions of earth, plant, animal, and man, are expressed in symptoms of decline and disease, which show us only too clearly that with our materialistic thoughts we have acted against the life-plans of God and now are faced with the consequences.

More or less unconsciously many human souls experience that their life slowly hardens and their organism becomes sclerotic. Man is in danger of becoming too much like a root—which strives too deeply into earthly conditions. Materialistic thinking has not enabled him at the same time to strive upwards like the other part of the plant. The plant does not consist only of root, just as man does not consist only or head. We can free ourselves out of this root condition only if our thinking can also grow upward. Only there is this difference, that the growing of our thought has no limit, it can grow up to the heavens and find there the spiritual soil of all earthly forms.

---

[10]   First appeared in the Sunfield Letters 1940.

When we follow the life aim for which the plant leaves strive, we are led to the planets. And if we ask for the inner sense of the word "planet" it reveals to us, as in the word "plant". The word "plan" (which means "design") and teaches us that the spiritual images of the life-plans of God are pictured in the planets. Also the planets form together a gigantic organism—its heart is the sun, the cosmic light, whose rays have no other striving than in selflessness to bear life down to earth.

In the plant world the light appears again in its purest and most concentrated form in the corn, which reveals the living gold of the sun in the plant. If we eat our bread with consciousness we know that we take in the forces of earth and heaven at the same time.

In this way we find again the certainty which we have lost in materialism, namely, that the Spiritual underlies all physical appearances—With this we find the inner strength to plough the soil of our thinking, and to cultivate life-filled thoughts so that earth, pant, animal and man can work together with the universe as one living organism.

THE FEEDING OF THE SMALL CHILD[11]

The feeding of the small child should be entirely adapted to the process of the child's development. After birth and descent into earthly existence, the child is still quite strongly connected with the heavens, from whence he has just come. Not until the first food has been taken, does the relationship with the Earth begin.

The first food of the child is the mother's milk. It is the most ideal food for the child because it contains, in the right proportions, all the nutriments which the child needs for building up his body, such as:

- Sugar,
- Albumen,
- Fats,
- Carbohydrates,
- Various Salts,
- Iron and Copper...

Substances are always the outward expression of something spiritual—*forms* are the outward expression of the creative Cosmic Word, out of which everything has originated and always will originate.

When the little child awakes out of his cosmic slumber—and he awakes but slowly, since otherwise he would be overwhelmed by the earthly impressions—than he needs to be received by forces, which belong to the world out of which he has come, otherwise the child would feel God-forsaken.. The child cries—he cries for his heavenly companions—for food. If the mother can develop a loving understanding for this, then she offers the child her breast, and with the milk which the baby takes in, all the heavenly companions enter. In their working together, there sounds the heavenly choir of starry harmonies, calling the soul down to earth, with loving voices:

Food

> Come! O Come! O Human Soul
> O! We ask you down to Earth
> Where we each in our Form
> God in His creation serve
> Come! O Human Soul.

---

[11] Notes date unknown.

Thus calls the food! The child hears the call and answers:
Digestion
Yes! I Come
Your blissful melody
Returns to me the starry harmony
The answer to your quest I give
God will I serve—as long I live.
Forgotten is my longing pain
Since you connected me again
With my sweet heaven.

Thus the cosmic forces, which are inherent in the mother's milk, when the child for the earthly existence in a healthy way, and we can now understand the bliss and satisfaction which the child experiences when taking in these forces. In listening to these heavenly voices and having answered them, the child has come into touch with the earthly matter and has performed his first great deed. He must gently be led back again into the cosmic sleep, and the mother with her singing must rock the baby back into the cosmos. The rocking is a picture of the cosmic movement in which the soul moves during sleep. Thus in the first few months of the baby's life there is a gentle coming and going—and nothing should disturb this wonderful rhythm. Here the child should be accompanied by the understanding thoughts and anxious love of those in whose care he is.

The child must slowly be able to detach himself from his heavenly home—on no account should the child have to under-go the hardship of being pushed and forced into the earthly existence. This can happen through artificial feeding if the child has to be fed on cow's milk, it cannot be avoided that he is forcibly turned out of his cosmic dream and is thereby open to becoming hardened more quickly. Although the cow's milk also contains all life-substances, it contains them in proportions that are wholesome for an **animal**. Also the animal is more earthly than the human being. Cow's milk must first be specially prepared before it is suitable for the digestive forces of the child.

Up to the 6th month, the child should be fed only on the mother's milk. Then, (in some cases perhaps a little earlier) one can begin with plant food, that is to say with **fruit** such as orange or tangerine-juice. This kind of fruit contains strong sun forces, which are direct cosmic forces. Each time the child takes in more food, he incarnates more deeply into the earthly conditions. When the child takes fruit, he takes in soul forces, which, in a pure way, permeate the plant in the blossom and in the fruit, and these soul forces stimulate the child's soul to incarnate more and more into his body. If the child is forced into the earthly condition too strongly and too quickly (for instance by suddenly giving him meat-juice) he can receive such a shock that it can cause soul disturbance throughout his whole life.

The next step in the feeding of the child proceeds from fruit to *seeds*—carbohydrates—which are contained in the grains of corn. Wheat flour and oatmeal are made into thin porridge with the addition of cow's milk. We also add the first mineralising process in form of sugar. Cane sugar is the ideal sugar to be used, being produced out of the stem of the plant, since here the cosmic and earthly forces are in balance. Beet sugar would already connect the child too strongly with the earthly forces, and the chemical substances that are used for bleaching the beet sugar can cause digestive distur-bances. Farinaceous foods (meal foods) sweetened with cane sugar slowly bring the baby to earth in harmony with the physiological condition of his age.

We may now go on to *leaf-vegetables*, Purees made of sieved *salads, spinach, stems* and then proceed to *Root-vegetables*, which have the closest connection with the earthly forces, such as *carrots, beetroots, kohlrabi and cau-liflower*. To avoid flatulence one should always add a little fennel or caraway to these vegetables, and in the case of car-rots and beetroots one should also add sugar:

- Fruit,
- Seed,
- Leaves,
- Roots.

That is the order of nutrition, which humanity followed in the course of evolution. First those parts of the plant were used which are *above* the earth then those parts that grow *under* the earth.

At this early stage of infancy *meat* is quite unsuitable, (except in some cases of illness) as the child becomes too strongly connected with the earthly forces. He would be cut off from cosmic influences and deprived of forces, which could never be replaced in later life. One should not be sur-

126

prised if, when they get older, the children become restless and nervous, as they have not been equipped with sufficient strength to protect themselves against the overwhelming influences and impressions of our present-day life. Children under two years old should live under the sheltering blue mantle of the Madonna, that is, protected by cosmic forces .

Gradually the use of milk gets less and less and after one year, not more than one pint a day is necessary. After carbohydrates have been introduced into the food, one can soon begin with *fats*. Small quantities of fresh butter (not margarine or similar artificial fats) may be added to the vegetables. Fat is necessary to keep the inner processes active albumen on the other hand has more forming power. Fat however, can only be properly digested by the child when he begins to unfold his own warmth activity, because these are the forces that he needs to assimilate fat, that is when he begins to raise himself, gradually learns to stand up and then starts to walk.

If the child tends towards constipation, which means he is unable to develop sufficient warmth, then one should give him substances that have been permeated with sun warmth, *e.g.*, honey, malt extract. (Roasting is also a warmth process.) If however there is a tendency towards diarrhoea, one can help by giving milk enriched with albumen, as this contains more formative forces.

❀ ❀ ❀

After the child's *first* year has passed, with help of his teeth which begin to develop; he will be able to manage more solid food. The milk may be reduced to a ½ pint per day, and it is necessary that the child learns to chew crusts of bread, rusks, biscuits, *etc.*

After the **third year** the child may eat the same food as taken by adults, except for greasy foods, eggs, alcohol, meat, mushrooms and certain spices. Meat, mushrooms and alcohol would bind the infant too strongly to the earth, whilst eggs on the other hand would lead him too much away from earthly conditions. Spices such as pepper, paprika, should be avoided, as they appeal to forces, which, have not yet developed in the child. Also the child is not yet ready for tea and coffee.

Up to the **seventh year** cosmic forces help the child to build up his body. With the change of teeth the building-up of the body gradually ends. The forces that hitherto were used for the completion of the body are now free to be used for the development of the soul-forces of the child, *i.e.*, Thinking, Feeling and Willing. (Memory—skilfulness of the limbs).

Children with **large heads** have not been able to detach themselves properly from their cosmic existence (embryonic stage). They are mostly inattentive, superficial and confused in their thinking their ideas are unclear. They often have red faces. In these cases it is necessary to stimulate the head forces by giving the children food taken from **roots.**

Contrary to the children with large heads, there are the pale children with **small heads.** They are over-intellectual, sharp, fond of analysing, and easily irritated by outer impressions. They have no imagination and have difficulties in doing anything artistic. This child needs more food of a flower-like nature, sweet and aromatic fruit, *etc.* They need food that draws them away from the earth. One can also add vegetables containing iron, such as spinach, nettles, *etc.* After their seventh year, these children may also have more spices.

When the child is **seven years old**, the soul-forces must be allowed to develop unhindered, and the child's constitution has now also reached the stage where it is ready for school-life. During this time, it is of special importance to give food consisting of leaves and stems, because from these parts of the plant **living** forces are released, which have a helpful influence on the thinking. (Roots make the thinking rigid therefore highly intellectual people mostly avoid roots and those who have to do a great deal of mental work mostly refuse to eat potatoes.) On the other hand, leaves stimulate the circulation processes, which at this age are especially active.

Milk should now only be taken in small quantities. Cocoa will also be found beneficial, if the digestive process is too active. However, one should be careful to give cocoa only in moderate quantities, because it makes the thinking slow and dull.

At this stage Meat should only be given in exceptional cases, where the child has lost considerable weight or suffers from weakness, or to children who are dreamy and sleepy and do not want to come down to Earth. Also sweet fruits and lemon juice will help these children to get wider awake. With regard to meat, one must take into consideration that white meat is not so earthly as the so-called red meat, as for instance, beef.

❀ ✿ ❀

Thus we are able to form a diet based on a physiological understanding of the child and of the human being as such. We realise that we must not only bear in mind the substances, Albumen, Carbohydrates, Fats, *etc.* We must also consider out of which kingdom they have been taken. That is to say whether they are animal, plant or mineral, blossom, leaf or root, and whether they are to be roasted, baked or boiled, and whether the food is to be served hot or cold.

Children with straight, dark hair should have sulphuric food, a great deal of blossoms and food that has been roasted. Hot food contains more sulphur than cold food.

Children with red, curly hair, however, should eat a lot of roots, and food containing iron. With these children the sulphuric forces tend to go too much to the head. They should have more cold meals. In order to teach children to eat foods that they do not like but which are necessary for them, one should always add to the food a little of something they especially like. It is not good to stuff children with eggs and farinaceous food, as this makes them less capable of learning. Instead they should eat a great deal of vegetables and salad.

Reference to eating of **eggs** before the age of two years. In this case the child loses the capacity to know what food is harmful and what food is beneficial, and just eats **everything**.

The different **temperaments**, especially if they are very one-sided, are of great importance with regard to nutrition. In school the teacher is able to influence the temperament of the child but unless he is assisted by a wholesome diet based on a real understanding of the child, his efforts will have little success. Also the opposite may be the case, and we see that much depends upon the co-operation of parents and teacher. They are the educators of the child, working from opposite directions through a mutual understanding—the teaching works from the head down into the body (from the

129

spirit into the form)—the nutrition from the body into the head (from the form into the spirit).

The Sanguine temperament is like the air, hastens from one impression to another, is interested in everything, but never wants to penetrate deeply into a thing the child is superficial. Such children need food which activates their metabolic system, so that they have to do something thoroughly, otherwise this part of their organism could get ill.

The Choleric temperament must treat his **Rhythmical System** thoroughly. Such children live too strongly in their body and explode like a fire flame. Their diet requires all green vegetables, cucumbers, melons—watery cool fruit helps to quench the fire; and make the child cool and brings him into a rhythmical condition.

The Phlegmatic temperament is little interested in the outer life and is chiefly occupied with his own thought-life. Such children need stimulating food, especially roots—which, owing to the amount of salt they contain, rouse the thinking. Very little liquid should be taken, because the child already has a watery, inactive constitution. Spicy salads, radishes, horse-radish, fruit, hot spices, such as ginger, mustard, *etc.* will be helpful.

The Melancholic temperament needs a lot of sunshine to bring him out of his moods, and such food as will draw him away from the earth. He should eat blossoms and food of a flower-like nature; the food should be colourful and look exquisite. Happy food and as much sugar as they like.

Melancholic children should *laugh* when they eat.

Phlegmatic children, however, should have *tears* in their eyes, caused by the hot fiery food they are eating.

The Sanguine child with his air-like tendencies must kindle the fire of his metabolism and the

Choleric child must quench the fire of his outbreaks with water and must make use of this fire in the right place by digesting roots, salads, *etc.* This is how his superabundance of strength should be used up.

Children, who have **grown too quickly**, need warmth-giving food, which stimulates the circulation of the blood.

Small children who have **not grown enough** and whose blood circulation is too strong, are in need of the form-giving forces of roots.

Tall and thin children are too much root.

Small and fat children are too much fruit and here we have to create the balance.

All that has been said, shows that nutrition cannot be separated from the nature of man.

ROSE ELIXIR

Elixir can be made at home and with roses or other flowers and fruit in the following manner:

A large open necked jar, a sweet jar is good and sterilise by heat.

Make a syrup with equal parts by volume of sugar/honey (for the type of sugar see introduction), to spring water. The water is warmed to dissolve the sugar, then left to cool.

When cool fill the jar about ¾, then add scented rose petals, dark red is best for colour, taking care to remove the white or yellow tips, as they may give a bitter taste, stir well. More petals may be added for up to three days.

The jar and its contents should then be put in direct sunlight from 6 am to 10 am then again from 4 pm to 7 pm each day. During the times of midday and night it should be put in the dark.. Each time it is brought out in to the sunlight it should be stirred.

This is repeated every day for 7 days after the last petals are added.

Then strain and decant into small sterilised bottles for storage. The sun should sterilise the elixir, but sometimes they can begin to ferment, if this happens remove tops and place the bottles in a pan of water and heat gently to boil off the alcohol then reseal

It is wise to make juices and elixirs for babies and young children with fructose or lactose as this is less harmful to teeth.

132

EPILOGUE

HERBS IN AGRICULTURE

What is *wholesome* food? The answer to this question presents us with a comprehensive and wide-ranging concept. Apart from its preparation in the kitchen, *wholesome* food also involves the cultivation of the soil for its production, and again this is linked up with its environment, including the whole universe.

With this in view we may, from a certain aspect, consider our obviously mounting food crisis, and we come to the conclusion that today not only man but fundamentally also the soil is suffering from hunger and deficiency, and as the one is dependent on the other, both are in need of help —that means of *wholesome* food. But this need can no longer be fully met, for such food is well on the way to passing out of existence.

For many years now we have lived through a period in which, by inorganic means, the steadily rising mineralisation and hardening processes of the living fertile soil have overruled our former methods of nourishing the soil with the life-encouraging forces of organic matter. Now we find ourselves in a dilemma where we can no longer stand aside as onlookers, for the time is drawing ever nearer when the deteriorating cover of the Earth will no longer be fit to maintain the life of mankind on this planet Earth.

However, as long as we can behold a *Light of Hope* we need not fear, for when we look back over the course of the twentieth century we find that this *Light* was already being 3 kindled at Whitsuntide 1924 when Rudolf Steiner* gave a course of lectures to farmers and gardeners on the subject of *Agriculture.* After his death and following many years of experimental work and practice, these lectures have been handed down to us to be used for the benefit of mankind.

By now the results of Rudolf Steiner's teaching and its practical application at home and abroad have been widely recognised and accepted by many who have found help in renewing soil-fertility as well as in all other branches of agriculture.

This is, of course, not the place to enlarge on so far-reaching a subject, but it may be of interest to the reader to know of the existence of the remedies prescribed for the unnatural sickening and hardening of the skin of the earth. The *Bio-Dynamic Preparations*, as they are called, also contain various kinds of our wild herbs, such as the Dandelion (*Taraxacum*), Camomile (*Matricaria chamomilla*), Nettles (*Urtica*), and others.

According to Rudolf Steiner, these herbs are particularly receptive to super-earthly, cosmic influences. For these influences to enter into earthly conditions they require a suitable vessel into which they can be received. This particular kind of vessel can be created only by a mediating power between earth and heaven—and this is man himself —by building a compost or manure heap into which these herbal preparations are inserted, that is, into the decaying organic matter. There they remain closed up until the decomposition process of the heap has been completed and it is ready to be used for providing the soil with natural and healthy home-made food, food that has been made whole.

Pondering on that *mysterious* compost heap we come to the recognition that its quality, its wholeness rests entirely on the fact that the one who is devoting himself to the care of compost or manure is waking up in his own consciousness to the affinity between earth and heaven. He realises the tremendous distance he has to overcome that marks the separation between macrocosmos and microcosmos. It seems so far and yet so near for their re-unification, in which the most distant meets with the nearest, the highest with the lowest, the greatest with the smallest. This reveals itself also in the participation of the elemental powers of earth, water, air and warmth as well as of the animal world, the plant sphere with its healing herbs, and the mineral kingdom. All together they are co-operative in the creation of a synthesis that holds the precious quintessence of *wholesome* food.

What has been severed—shall be made whole. These words are written in golden letters in every human heart, and in times to come we shall recognise their reality.

In this sense today, when matter is becoming an empty vessel without the fullness of the healing Spirit, we value all the more Rudolf Steiner's endowment to Agriculture, the contents of which give every landowner, husbandman or smallholder as well as all those engaged in horticulture, even in the smallest garden plot, the possibility to help in the field of nutrition by using Bio-Dynamic methods, thus ensuring the life of mankind on Earth.

BIBLIOGRAPHY

To Herbs in Nutrition

BAKER, Alma: Memorandum-"The Soil and its Products". An appeal to the Governments of all nations, with special reference to Rudolf Steiner's Bio-Dynamic Methods of Agriculture, June 1938.

BULFINCH, TH.: The Age of Fables. New York, 1935.

CULPEPER: Complete Herbal. 1653.

EMERSON, R. W.: Essays.

GERARD, JOHN: History of Pants. 1597.

GRIMM: Complete Fairy Tales.

GROHMANN, G.: The Plant. 1974.

HAUSCHKA: The Nature of Substance. London, 1966.
       "   Nutrition. London, 1967.

PELIKAN: Healing Plants. Reprinted from the British Homeopathic Journal for Rudolf Steiner Press. 1956.

PFEIFFER, E. E.: Die Fruchtbarkeit der Erde. 1956.

PRATT: Plants of Great Britain.

STEINER, Rudolf: Agriculture. English Translation, 1958.

WACHSMUTH, G.: Etheric Formative Forces in Cosmos, Earth and Man. London, 1932.

LIST OF BOOKS FOR FURTHER READING

The following are available from; *Anastasi Mail Order Book Service:*

By other publishers:

UNDERSTAND YOUR TEMPERAMENT! A GUIDE TO THE FOUR TEMPERAMENTS: CHOLERIC, SANGUINE, PHLEGMATIC, MELANCHOLIC, by *Dr. Gilbert Childs*
ISBN 1-85584-025-1 £9.95

WORK ON THE LAND AND THE CONSTELLATIONS, by *Maria Thun*, a guide for calendar users,
ISBN 0-906155-30-X £3.90.

Companion to;

WORKING WITH THE STARS, A BIO-DYNAMIC SOWING AND PLANTING CALENDAR, by *Maria & Matthias K. Thun*, including advice for beekeepers.
Usually available late December early January orders taken all year. £3.90

THE EVER CHANGING GARDEN, by *Arne Klingborg*
ISBN 0-906155-12-6 £12.85

THE NATURE OF SUBSTANCE, by *Rudolf Hauschka*,
ISBN 0-85440-424-4 £8.95

THE PLANT VOL. 1, by *Gerbert Grohmann*
ISBN 0-938250-23-X £10.95.

THE PLANT VOL. 2, by *Gerbert Grohmann*
ISBN 0-938250-24-8 £10.95.

BIO-DYNAMIC GARDENING, by *John Soper*
ISBN 0275-63279-5 £TBA

THE EARTH'S FACE, ecological land-management and conservation by *Ehrenfried Pfeiffer*,
ISBN 0-906155-24-X £5.95

BIODYNAMIC AGRICULTURE RUDOLF STEINER'S IDEAS IN PRACTICE, by *Willy Schilthuis*
ISBN 0-86315-178-7 £4.99

RUDOLF STEINER — SCIENTIST OF THE INVISIBLE, by *A. P. Shepherd*
ISBN 0-86315-518-9 £6.99

AGRICULTURE, by *Rudolf Steiner.*
ISBN 0-938-250-37-1 £12.50

THE SCIENCE OF KNOWING by *Rudolf Steiner.*
ISBN 0-936132-97-3 £8.25.
HOW TO KNOW HIGHER WORLDS, by *Rudolf Steiner.*
ISBN 0-88010-372-8 £6.95
THEOSOPHY, by *Rudolf Steiner*
ISBN 0-88010-373-6 £8.95
METAMORPHOSES OF THE SOUL VOL. 1 by *Rudolf Steiner.*
ISBN 0-85440-414-7 £7.50
METAMORPHOSES OF THE SOUL VOL. 2 by *Rudolf Steiner.*
ISBN 0-85440-415-5 £7.50

Books published by Anastasi:
THE BATTLE FOR THE SPIRIT, *the Church & Rudolf Steiner*,
by Ven. A. P. Shepherd DD.
ISBN 0-9524403-0-X £9.95
SONGS OF SUNFIELD 1930 — 1940 JUBILEE EDITION 1990,
ISBN 0-9524403-1-8 £9.95
WATERCOLOURS RICH AND STRANGE, *Watercolour Paintings*
by Alec Morison. **Brochure** to an exhibition at Wolverhampton.
ISBN 0-9524403-2-6 £2.00.
Also available a Print of THETIS £8.32, and a Poster for
the exhibition at Wolverhampton featuring POLARITY
No. 1 £5.00 both by Alec Morison, size A3.
Forthcoming Titles;
The Water Lily & Peter with the big head by U. Grhal.
Bio-Dynamics. by Deryck Duffy
The Sunfield Plays
A Short History of Sunfield

All the above will be supplied subject to availability.
We reserve the right to change prices without notice.
Send no money now, please pay by return on receipt of your order.
Full refund can only be given if the goods are returned within 14
days and in a saleable condition on their arrival with us.
Allow 28 days for delivery.
UK P&P up to 15% on orders under £75.00, orders above £75.00
p&p free.
Overseas P&P at cost please state, air or surface mail.
Send your Orders to:
Anastasi Ltd. (H1), Broome, Nr. Stourbridge W. Mids., DY9
0HB UK.

Advertisements:

Elysia Natural Skin Care

Haselor, College Road
Bromsgrove, Worcestershire. B60 2NF
Tel / Fax 01527 832863

A Rose Elixir similar to Maria Geuter's is made by a company called *Wala Heilmittel* of Boll in Germany. They also manufacture anthroposphical remedies and the Dr Hauschka range of skin care products. The elixirs and skin care range are available by mail order from us and from selected outlets. Contact us for more information and credit card sales.

The Wala Elixirs

Wild flowers and berries are gathered at sunrise from unspoilt surroundings and added to fresh spring water and pure cane sugar or honey. The mixture is then exposed to the earth's natural rhythms of the rising and setting sun, warmth and cool, and light and dark. In this way the vital forces of the plant are preserved. The elixirs have specific tonic properties and a general harmonising effect upon our whole organism. They are suitable for all ages, and are especially helpful in times of exhaustion and convalescence.

Rose Petal Elixir Very harmonising and valuable in states of weakness and exhaustion. Particularly suitable for children.

Blackthorn Elixir Most effective in spring time or during convalescence as it restores tone and vitality to the organism.

Quince Elixir Beneficial for the lining of the respiratory tract and stomach.

Rowan Elixir An autumn tonic, protective and regulatory, particularly of the digestive processes.

Elderflower Elixir For the autumn and winter, helps protect against the cold and damp; good for coughs and colds.

Hawthorn Elixir Harmonising and strengthening of the circulatory processes, and after physical stress (eg. flu) and mental stress (eg. exams, insomnia).

Bitter Elixir Helps to activate the digestion; assists in re-harmonising the digestive processes after minor gastric upsets or dietary indiscretions.

Elysia Natural Skin Care

Haselor, College Road
Bromsgrove, Worcestershire. B60 2NF
Tel / Fax 01527 832863

Another range of products we stock, which may be of interest to readers of *Herbs in Nutrition*, is the Holle baby cereal range. These are bio-dynamically grown and have been used for decades by parents determined to feed their babies on the highest quality foods possible. They are available from us and selected outlets, please call us for more information and credit card sales.

Holle Baby Cereals

These products are just the basic cereal ingredients of a meal. Holle gives you the responsibility of adding milk, water and vegetable oil to the cereal in order to make up the meal so that it contains all the necessary nutrients for your child. This means that you know exactly what is in the feeds and can adapt them as necessary.

Babies cannot easily digest raw cereals as their digestive systems are still developing. *Holle Nahrmittel*, the Swiss manufacturers, have developed a special process in which the cereals are very slowly and gently heated, which makes them easier to digest but does not destroy their goodness.

NB. Breast feeding is the best way to feed a baby during the first 4-6 months of life. However, if for any reason this is not possible, then the Holle range can be used.

Holle Baby Rice This can be made up to a gluten-free bottle feed and can be very helpful throughout childhood as a porridge meal in cases of diarrhoea.

Holle Number 1 Contains wheat, barley and oats. Recommended as a bottle feed from the 4th month during the weaning phase. Can also make a porridge meal.

Holle Number 2 Contains wheat, barley and oats. Recommended as a porridge feed from 4 months. Natural fibres in the cereal encourage the digestive processes.

Holle Barley Cereal A cereal supplement for vegetable and fruit purees.

Holle Rusks A tasty snack.

Holle Whole Cane Sugar For mixing with the cereals, it is an unrefined sugar with trace elements and mineral salt content four times that of normal brown sugar. Very tasty on yoghurt too!

Anastasi Ltd.

Broome, Nr. Stourbridge W.M., Worcs., DY9 0HB, UK.

BOOK Publisher & Mail Order

Order Form:

Address
Mr./Mrs./Miss./Ms.
First Name(s)
Surname
Address
Town
County   Postcode
Tel.

Please supply

ty.	Title	Author	ISBN

We reserve the right to change prices without notice.

Send no money now, please pay by return on receipt of your order.

Full refund can only be given if the goods are returned within 14 days and in a saleable condition on their arrival with us.

Allow 28 days for delivery.

UK P&P up to 15% on orders under £75.00, orders above £75.00 p&p free.

Overseas P&P at cost please state, air or surface mail.

Signed .... Date.............